MW00612487

Quality Culture in the Pharmaceutical Industry

*Implementing a Behavior-based
Quality and Compliance Culture*

Quality Culture in the Pharmaceutical Industry

Implementing a Behavior-based Quality and Compliance Culture

Jose (Pepe) Rodríguez-Pérez, PhD

Copyright © 2021 José (Pepe) Rodríguez-Pérez
Business Excellence Consulting - BEC Press
All rights reserved.
ISBN-978-1-7367429-0-7

Passion for Quality

Business Excellence Consulting
PO Box 8326
Bayamón, PR 00960-8326 (USA)
www.bec-global.com
info@bec-global.com

Dedication

To my father Ginés and my father-in-law James
Thank you for your love, guidance and
wonderful conversations
We know you're near and in our hearts

Table of Contents

vii

List of Tables and Figures

Preface

We develop and manufacture medical products under a *quality management system*, for example ICH Q10 for pharmaceutical and biopharmaceutical or ISO 13485 for medical devices. We do not name them as quality leadership systems, and very probably, everyone reading this book appreciate that management and leadership are different. Managers oversee and optimize processes to deliver results. Leaders change (improve) those processes to deliver greater results. Companies need both, managers, and leaders as they are both necessary to produce and deliver safe and effective medical products to patients worldwide. The content of this book is aimed to the enhancement of the quality and compliance culture leadership within the medical product manufacturing industry.

Most of pharmaceutical manufacturing sites have adequate facilities and equipment, and, in many cases, quality products either novel products or generic versions but their quality systems are ill-implemented. Consequences are typically regulatory inspections showing broken quality systems and a lack of quality and compliance culture. Why? A single reason appears everywhere: people.

In most, if not in all cases, people in charge of the facility and those in command of the whole company are the biggest offenders and responsible for the inadequate compliance and quality culture.

We need better quality system management and more quality and compliance culture leadership. In short, the following enhancement elements can be identified:

People do not follow procedures when manufacturing and testing medical products.

Procedures and documentation are lacking enough and important details or, in many cases, are including many unnecessary information, notes, and so on.

Training programs are not well conceived nor adequately implemented and without a formal and adequate verification of the learning process.

Controls such as internal audits are not properly implemented.

Supervision is not adequate.

People competencies and personal development are not part of the training/human resources priorities.

Human errors are everywhere and the solely response at many companies is re-training (again and again) personnel.

And finally, the biggest problem is that **leaders/senior managers** are not doing enough to effectively solve all those problems. Micro-management or nano-management styles cannot solve the poor quality and compliance culture.

The idea of this book was surrounding me for several years. As the owner of a medium-size consulting company focused on assist worldwide medical product manufacturing companies struggling to meet the U.S. FDA quality system/GMP requirements, I saw all of the above symptoms acting together, in India, China, Japan, Europe, North America, South America, everywhere.

Very often, the response of regulated companies to regulatory enforcement is the same: hiring consultants to specifically remediate the regulators' findings, replacing some members of the staff, changing some procedures and provide some training. The results from these insufficient and expensive spot fixes? Successive violative inspections, warning letters, import alerts, consent decrees for U.S. companies, regulatory meetings, and so on.

I heard senior managers and owner of those companies claiming that they cannot believe that after expending a lot of money in such remediation activities they are still under import alert, consent decrees, and the likes.

The reason is clear: because they attacked symptoms but not the fundamental and primary root cause which is the *lack of adequate quality and compliance culture.*

So, the purpose of this book is to provide those leaders and senior managers with a clear roadmap to solve their regulatory problems and to return to the route of compliance by implementing a strong, positive quality and compliance culture. The recipe is clear and simple: all you need is good people, good procedures and good training programs sailing into a strong and positive culture of quality and compliance.

There was, and still is, an overemphasis on training and quality control activities, including inspections, to modify behaviors and achieve better results. This is largely based on the belief that the desired behavior change can be achieved by simply training employees and inspecting processes. Leaving aside the fact that most of training programs in our industry are ill-designed and rarely they include appropriate measurement of effectiveness. It should be recognized that both activities are important, but they are not enough to effectively change behaviors and achieve quality success. We must understand the complexity of behavior and analyze the causes of the performance problem (lack of skill, lack of motivation, ineffective work system, and so on) before proposing the right solution.

When a company implements a behavior-based quality and compliance culture they look into their problems as a whole, and they understand that there are multiple factors (including the soft ones related to personal and organizational behaviors) that affect performance. A very positive consequence of this systematic thinking is the shift from CAPA programs mostly correctives to ones where the systemic preventive actions are predominant.

Quality is everyone responsibility, but when it comes to creating, strengthening, or maintaining a culture within an organization, there is one group who really own it: the leaders and senior managers.

The good news is that creating or strengthening a positive and sustainable quality culture is an achievable task although not an easy or quick one.

In the first Chapter we present an introduction to the topic of quality and compliance culture and its critical implications in the world of medical product manufacture, including why it is necessary and how to enhance the QMS to a behavior-based quality culture. An effective and efficient quality system must be built on a solid quality and compliance culture foundation which, in turns, need also a very solid foundation. The foundation of any company is its values and principles and to be successful and build an effective quality culture the company must define culture as a foundational and core principle.

The second Chapter presents the ten principles of quality and compliance culture, from leadership at the top to accountability and commitment to resilience and learning from errors.

Chapter 3 describes the quality behaviors associated to each of the ten principles while Chapter 4 presents a comprehensive set of leading quality metrics to monitor three basic areas of quality culture: a) leadership engagement, b) people engagement, and c) culture and maturity.

Chapter 5 focus on people, the key element of everything, including quality and compliance culture. We will discuss elements such as hiring, engagement, supervision, and motivation, all of which are necessary elements for a solid human factor program.

Competence management and people development programs, formerly known as training programs, are discussed in Chapter 6. We will focus on it because it is one of key element of quality system and quality culture, and because more than 90% of CAPAs generated in this industry use training and retraining as the way to solve all our problems.

Chapter 7 covers procedures, instructions, records and the rest of CGMP documentation associated to a medical product manufacturing quality system, with a special focus on how to encourage good documentation practices and minimize the opportunity for human errors.

Chapter 8 discusses how to develop and enhance the leadership, as lack of adequate leadership represents the single, most important, and critical root cause for poor and inadequate quality culture.

Chapter 9 describes twelve areas ("The Dirty Dozen") where an overwhelming majority of pharmaceutical companies need a comprehensive overhaul to reduce their risk of lack of compliance.

Appendix A describes in a tabular form, the characteristics, desired behaviors, and leading indicators (metrics) that are associated to each of the ten principles of a strong, positive quality and compliance culture.

I hope you enjoy reading this book as much as I have enjoyed writing it. Always remember that

Quality culture is a long journey but not a chimera

Chapter 1
Introduction to Quality and Compliance Culture

Culture: from Latin cultus, which means care
Quality: from Latin qualitat-, qualitas equivalent to quāl(is) of what sort + -itās -ity
Compliance: from Latin complēre to complete, having all parts or elements, lacking nothing. In a legal context, this means to obey legal orders and fully realize the rule of law

M edical product manufacturers are critical to our way of living as demonstrated by the recent coronavirus pandemic. Diagnostic tests, medicines, preventive vaccines, protective personnel equipment (masks, face shields, gloves, gowns, and so on), hardware such as ventilators, and a very long list of other products, all became familiar household products these days as their shortages made opening news at many news outlets.

However, this critical industry is often plagued by errors, mistakes, data integrity breaches, and other issues that are linked to un-quality behaviors by their personnel. Laboratory failure investigations, manufacturing deviations, customer complaints, and other quality system records very often pointed toward inadequate behavior of employees as the root cause of those situations.

For many years, we considered human errors or mistakes as the cause of mishaps or problems. In the manufacturing industries, human error, under whatever label (procedures not followed, lack of attention, or simply human error), is the conclusion of many quality problem investigations. Very often it was coupled with some kind of training activity (most frequently retraining) as corrective action. We even have an old adage - *To err is human* - to try to explain this behavioral problem.

The way we look at the human side of problems has evolved during the past few decades. Industrial psychologists and human reliability professionals took command during the investigation of catastrophic accidents, such as the Chernobyl, *Challenger*, and aviation accidents, and our view on human error changed. Now we see human errors as the symptoms of deeper causes. In other words, human errors are consequences, not causes. We need to understand why people do not follow procedures if we want to fix it.

When a medical product manufacturer receives observations similar to the ones depicted below in Figure 1.1, at the end of a regulatory inspection, its quality system is broken, and its quality and compliance culture very poor. You cannot *effectively* fix that merely by firing a few people and providing some training to the rest. If you are in charge of the situation (probably you were hired to replace one of the fired managers), you will need to modify behaviors of (a few) people: investigators, reviewers, approvers, all the middle and top management of the site, including the whole quality unit, and the division/company leaderships who allowed this situation to exist. All of them are responsible for that. Replacing all of them is the solution? No, because you would be attacking the symptom (un-quality behavior) not the real root cause, which is the inadequate (or absent) quality and compliance culture.

- *Your firm failed to thoroughly investigate any unexplained discrepancy or failure of a batch or any of its components to meet any of its specifications, whether or not the batch has already been distributed. Your firm did not adequately investigate product failures and significant defect complaints.*

- *You lacked thorough investigations into root causes and failed to implement prompt and effective corrective actions and preventive actions (CAPA).*

- *You failed to conduct adequate investigations into out-of-specification (OOS) test results for critical product attributes, such as assay, for your products.*

- *Your investigations into the OOS results did not determine root causes and include effective corrective action and preventive action (CAPA) to prevent their recurrence.*

- *Your rationales for invalidating the testing failures lacked a substantive scientific evaluation.*

- *Your firm did not adequately investigate drug product failures to ensure that you did not release defective drug product.*

Figure 1.1 Typical U.S. FDA citations related to investigation and CAPA programs

Improving the quality of our products and the compliance of our processes requires going beyond traditional training, testing and inspectional approaches to manage risks. It requires a better understanding of the company culture and the human dimension of quality and compliance in our highly regulated industry. If we want to improve the quality of our products and the compliance of our processes, we must change the way people do things. We must change people's behaviors by implementing a behavior-based quality management system and by extension a behavior-based quality and compliance culture.

If you want to manage the quality culture of your organization or simply, you desperately need to improve the quality and compliance level of your group, first you must understand what quality culture is, what content it covers and how to assess it. Culture and leadership are two sides of the same coin and one cannot understand one without the other[1].

So, this book is for you, leader of a pharmaceutical or medical product manufacturing company who need to enhance the quality and compliance culture of your organization. If you are the quality or manufacturing site manager, the head of a company's division or you occupy the C-corner of your corporate building, the following pages will provide you valuable insights on how to become a change agent and create and sustain a strong, positive *quality and compliance culture.*

1.1 What is Quality Culture

In short, it can be defined as what your organization stands for quality, what is the purpose of your organization in terms of quality. The purpose (why you are in business) of any organization is to serve customers. The quality culture determines how both, employees and customers view an organization.

Organizational culture refers to the beliefs and behaviors that determine how employees and management interact and handle beyond-organization transactions. Often, culture is implied, not expressly defined, and develops over time from cumulative traits of the people who are involved. In some cases, it can be the results of the personality and philosophy of a powerful and influential leader.

However, as Schein mentioned, "the biggest danger in trying to understand culture is to oversimply it". Schein describes three levels of culture (Figure 1.2) ranging from the very visible to the very tacit and almost invisible.

Schein describes culture as the way we do things at our company or our values and principles is a mistake because these are manifestations of the culture, but these are not the culture at the levels where culture matters.

Schein's model of organizational culture originated in the 1980s. Schein (2010) identifies three distinct levels in organizational cultures, related to the degree to which the different cultural phenomena are visible to the observer.

---

[1]Schein, Edgar H. 2009. *The Corporate Culture Survival Guide.* San Francisco: Jossey-Bass.

Three Levels of Culture

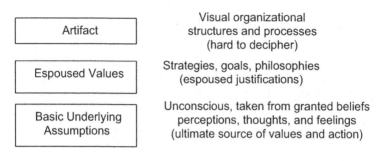

Figure 1.2 The Three Levels of Culture

- **Artifacts** include any tangible, overt or verbally identifiable elements in any organization. Architecture, furniture, dress code, even office jokes, all exemplify organizational artifacts. Artifacts are the visible elements in a culture, and they can be recognized by people who is not part of the culture. Other typical artifacts are:

  - Level of formality in authority relationships

  - Working hours

  - Meetings (how often, how run, timing)

  - How are decision made?

  - Communications: How do you learn stuff?

  - Social events

  - Jargon, identity symbols

  - Rite and rituals

  - Disagreement and conflicts: How are they handled?

- Balance between work and family

At the level of artifacts, culture is very clear and recognizable, but you do not know why the member of the organization are behaving as they do and why the organization is constructed as it is. To understand the culture, you must decipher what is happening at the next deeper level.

- **Espoused values** are the organization's stated values and rules of behavior. It is how the members represent the organization both to themselves and to others. This is often expressed in official philosophies and public statements of identity. It can sometimes be a projection for the future, of what the members hope to become. Examples of this would-be employee professionalism, or a "family first" mantra. Trouble may arise if espoused values by leaders are not in line with the deeper tacit assumptions of the culture. Typical espoused values are:

  - Integrity

  - Teamwork

  - Customer orientation

  - Product quality

When you analyze organizations, you will detect obvious inconsistences between some of the espoused values and the visible behavior. What these inconsistences demonstrate is that a deeper level of thought and perception is driven the overt behavior. Again, to be able to understand the culture, you must decipher what is happening at the deeper level.

- **Underlying assumptions** are shared basic assumptions that are the deeply embedded, taken-for-granted behaviors which are usually unconscious but constitute the essence of culture. These assumptions are typically so well integrated in the company's dynamic that they are hard to recognize from within. The essence of culture is the jointly learned values and beliefs that work so well that they become shared and taken for granted as the organization continues to growth.

In our industry, an underlying and basic assumption is that the quality of our products is not negotiable and that we cannot cut corner to reduce costs. To do that we only need to remove waste (rework, rejections, deviations, and so on) and inefficiencies from our processes.

Even though the quality of our products and the compliance of our processes is everyone's responsibility, it's the main and most critical responsibility of leaders and managers to reinforce and be role models for quality and compliance actions.

So, answering the original question of what quality culture is, we can say that quality and compliance culture is how the employees in a company or organization think about quality, it is the quality behaviors that they routinely practice and show.

Below information was part of a banner at the main entrance of a sterile drug manufacturing site:

"Appreciate your efforts for following the Good Documentation Practices and the principles of ALCOA for Data Integrity"

The integrity of data is not an option. It is a very basic and foundational value of any organization, and it is even more crucial in our industry where the life of patients can be compromised due to lack of accuracy and integrity. In addition, data integrity is a global mandatory requirement for the regulated medical product industry. It is more than a mere expectation. However, the content of this banner is watched daily by hundreds of employees who are thanked by their leaders for *trying* to comply with this absolute requirement. The conveyed message is far from the regulatory and legal requirement that all data *must* have integrity.

In addition, the importance of a quality and compliance culture in the prevention and mitigation of human failures (errors, mistakes, and violations) cannot be ignored. A good organizational culture will serve to reduce human error.

The effects of cultural and even demographic factors in system operations are evident. Organizational culture can influence a wide variety of operator–equipment interactions and can make the difference between effective and erroneous performance. Even among companies seemingly devoted to enhancing operational performance and safety, organizational culture can have a potentially adverse effect in achieving quality and safety. As an example, the *New York Times* reported on poor organizational practices in the National Aeronautics and Space Administration (NASA) in an article titled "Poor Management by NASA Is Blamed for Mars Failure":

> The Mars Polar Lander spacecraft probably failed last year because its descent engine shut down prematurely, but the mission's loss can ultimately be attributed to inadequate management, testing, and financing, independent experts told NASA today.
> In candid reports assessing recent problems with the National Aeronautics and Space Administration's program to explore Mars, two panels concluded that pressures to conform to the agency's recent credo of "faster, cheaper, better" ended up compromising ambitious projects. To meet the new constraints, the report said, project managers sacrificed needed testing and realistic assessments of the risk of failure.[2]

The article also indicates that NASA management had been criticized for many of the same management practices and norms demonstrated after the 1986 Space Shuttle Challenger accident, noting that:

> Several recent panels have suggested the new approach may have gone too far by emphasizing cost-cutting and tight schedules at the price of quality.

On the other hand, in an article about the retail giant Costco Wholesale published December 15, 2016, in Fortune[3], the author mentioned that "everyone at Costco will tell you that its culture comes directly from Jim Sinegal," Costco's cofounder and its CEO from 1983 to 2012. The author also mentioned that for Sinegal "Culture is not the most important thing. It's the only thing."

---

[2]https://archive.nytimes.com/www.nytimes.com/library/national/science/0 32900sci-nasa-mars.html, accessed 02/03/2021

[3]https://fortune.com/longform/costco-wholesale-shopping/,accessed 2/3/2021

The article credited Costco's cofounder with creating a management style that was based on an informal, unintimidating environment in which no one was afraid of making mistakes. Sinegal had another inviolate value proposition: "Inexpensive couldn't mean cheap, because he knew Costco would lose customers that way. Quality, quality, quality."

If we analyze how organizations are dealing with safety culture to prevent accidents, we will have a great benchmark for preventing errors affecting quality as well. Inquiries into major accidents have found faults in the organizational structures and procedures. These were judged to be as important as the technical and individual human failures. There is now an emphasis on the need for organizations to improve their safety culture.

Earlier in my career I was involved in an analysis of several thousand batches of medical products produced at one FDA-regulated plant. Not a single event was ever documented related to component(s) spilled prior to charging the mixing tanks. However, more than 40 batches had document deviations (out-of-specification analysis results) due to concentration of one or more of their components below specifications. Surely, many (if not most) of these failures were a consequence of some material being spilled prior to its addition to the bulk tank. Failures and subsequent investigations and product rejections could have been avoided if the operator(s) had notified supervisors about the spill and requested more components. Instead, fear of retaliation and punishment led them to hide these situations. Needless to say, each of those 40 failure investigations was a nightmare; laboratory results showed lack of adequate quantity of components, while pristine manufacturing batch documentation showed that everything was perfect!

Every group of people develops a "culture": shared attitudes, beliefs, and ways of behaving. In an organization with a good compliance and quality culture, everyone puts those elements high on the list. Everyone shares accurate perceptions of the risks to compliance and quality and adopts the same positive attitudes to compliance and quality. This influences the ways in which individuals in the group handle new events and decisions. The compliance and quality culture of an organization is an important factor in controlling human failures.

Returning to our medical product manufacturing environment, why would an experienced manufacturing operator not properly document

CGMP data he or she generated? What would motivate a 10-year veteran employee to enter a clearly labeled manufacturing area without wearing the required gowning vest?

Following is an extract from a recent FDA Warning Letter to a company missing any sign of effective quality and regulatory compliance culture:

> The garbing (consisting of face masks, hair nets, gloves, and suits without hoods) used at your facility is not adequate to protect the drug product from microbiological contamination during sterile processing. During your demonstration of cleaning and disinfection practices for your aseptic processing room, our investigators observed an operator who wore eye makeup with no eye protection.
>
> The operators wore clothing that allowed for exposed skin on their faces and necks. Furthermore, personnel reused these suits on multiple aseptic processing production days, with no cleaning or sterilization between uses. Rather than instructing operators to dispose of used suits after each use, the procedure your firm used at the time of the inspection instructed cleanroom operators to "store the suit in a clean place for next entry." Your failure to ensure that personnel wear clothing appropriate to protect the drug product from contamination increases the significant risk to product sterility in your aseptic processing operation.[4]

High reliability organizations (HROs) are organizations that operate for long periods under difficult conditions and have few major safety incidents. As defined in Weick et al. (1999) "the processes found in the best HROs provide the cognitive infrastructure that enables simultaneous adaptive learning and reliable performance." The five key elements discussed there are summarized below:

a) Preoccupation with failures rather than success. Being wary of long periods of success and encouraging identification of early signs of failures.

---

[4]https://www.fda.gov/ICECI/EnforcementActions/WarningLetters/2016/ucm507554.htm, accessed 2/03/2021

b) Reluctance to simplify interpretations. Steps are taken to create a more complete and detailed understanding of what is going on.

c) Sensitivity to operations. Managers are sensitive to the experiences of their frontline operators and discuss their perceptions of the operation with them.

d) Commitment to resilience. Errors will occur, and the organization should have systems to identify, correct, and learn from errors, and be focused on continually developing people's skills and knowledge.

e) Deference to expertise. Decisions are taken by people with the greatest expertise, even if they are low in the organizational hierarchy.

1.2 Characteristics of a culture of quality

While no medical product regulations currently incorporate explicit requirements for a quality culture, different organizations such as the American Society for Quality (ASQ), the Parenteral Drug Association (PDA) and the International Society for Pharmaceutical Engineering (ISPE) begun several years ago to work with the concept of quality culture, specifically applied to the pharmaceutical manufacturing industry in the case of PDA and ISPE. Both organizations initiated their efforts when the U.S. FDA published its first draft guidance on the subject of quality metrics in July 2015[5]. This request for quality metrics was an offspring of the Food and Drug Administration Safety and Innovation Act (FDASIA) Public Law No. 112-144 approved in July 2012. Under the Title VII of FDASIA, the FDA may require the submission of any records or other information that FDA may inspect under section 704 of the FD&C Act, in advance or in lieu of an inspection, by requesting the records or information from a person that owns or operates an establishment that is engaged in the manufacture, preparation, propagation, compounding, or processing of a drug.

---

[5]Food and Drug Administration (FDA). 2015. *Request for Quality Metrics. Guidance for Industry*. Draft Guidance. Washington: FDA

However, the U.S. FDA is talking about quality culture from a while, and those talks increased with the adoption, in April 2009, of ICH Q10 which provides a harmonized model for a pharmaceutical quality system (PQS). The ICH Q10 PQS aligned CGMP with basic business goals of process predictability (for example, right first-time initiatives) and product reliability. The implementation of *Quality by Design* or the pioneer implementation of the 2011 guidance for industry related to process validation are another strong signal in this direction with the emphasis on better design and proactive monitoring of processes. The following eight characteristics of pharmaceutical quality culture were presented by FDA in 2011[6]:

1. Science-based approaches

2. Decisions based on understanding product's intended use

3. Proper identification and control of areas of potential process weakness (including raw materials)

4. Responsive deviation and investigation systems that lead to timely remediation

5. Sound methods for assessing risk

6. Well-defined and designed processes and products, from development through entire product life cycle

7. Systems for careful analyses of product quality

8. Supportive management (philosophically and financially)

The American Society for Quality (ASQ) and Forbes published in 2014 a global study entitled Culture of Quality[7]. This first-of-its-kind global study offers actionable insight into how a more quality driven

---

[6] https://www.fda.gov/media/82570/download, accessed 2/03/2021
[7] ASQ/Forbes Insights. 2014. *Culture of Quality – Accelerating growth and performance in the enterprise.* New Work: Forbes Insights

culture can accelerate business performance. Its remarks that a strong culture of quality is a key component to an organization's success.

Among the main components of a culture of quality, this study includes:

- Clearly visible, engaged and unwavering senior management support for quality initiatives

- Clearly articulated vision and values

- Active and ongoing engagement with customers to continually identify and address current and evolving needs

- Clearly stated quality goals

- Performance expectations for all individuals throughout the company that clearly link to quality goals

- Appropriate incentives, which can favor monetary or recognition-based awards, depending on individual circumstances

PDA Survey - 2014 Quality Culture Metrics[8]

This PDA study was the first one specifically focused on the pharmaceutical industry. PDA included in this survey a list of behaviors based on seven characteristics of quality culture identified by participants at the 2013 PDA Pharmaceutical Metric Conference. Those characteristics are:

- Communication and transparency

- Commitment and engagement

- Technical excellence

- Standardization of criteria or requirements

[8]PDA. 2015. *PDA Survey: 2014 Quality Culture Metric*. Bethesda: PDA

- Cross-functional vision

- Rewards and recognition

- Speak up for quality culture

ISPE's Cultural Excellence Report[9]
This report shares insights on quality culture improvement across six key dimensions and outlines a series of practical and powerful approaches, practices, and tools to support implementation of the cultural excellence framework and promote behavioral change that will ultimately benefit the patient and the business.

The report focuses on the six dimensions of cultural excellence, a framework introduced at the ISPE Quality Metrics Summit in April 2015 that facilitates a holistic assessment of those elements required to foster, develop, monitor, measure, learn, and ultimately improve an organization's quality culture.

The six dimensions are:

- **Leadership and vision:** Leaders establish and engender the vision for the organization. Their thoughts, words, and actions about quality are critical in establishing and maintaining a culture of operational excellence. Leadership and vision, therefore, play a key role in establishing the culture, either within a local manufacturing site or across the company.

- **Mindset and attitudes**: These play a key role in driving cultural performance, although they can be difficult to define, observe, and measure. Leaders can assess, monitor, and develop the desired cultural excellence mindset and attitudes within their organizations, using the practical and powerful approaches outlined in this report.

- **Gemba walks:** Management engagement on the floor is a powerful way to demonstrate quality commitment to all members of the organization. Gemba walks allow site leaders to communicate clear messages using open and honest dialogue and provide a real

[9]ISPE. 2017. *Culture Excellence Report April 2017*. Bethesda: ISPE

indication of progress toward desired behaviors at all levels. Gemba walks also empower front-line employees by recognizing their contributions to site results and involving them in problem-solving and continuous improvement.

- **Leading quality indicators and triggers**: There are inherent links between culture, behavior, and leading quality indicators (LQIs) that drive desired patient-focused behaviors. Monitoring and surveillance of key triggers and the design of LQIs are highly recommended practices to help shape cultural excellence.

- **Oversight and review**: Management oversight and review practices that engage both management and employees support a healthy quality culture because they demonstrate transparency, facilitate dialogue, bring attention to issues so they can be addressed, and highlight best practices so they can be replicated.

- **Structural enablers:** These support the desired behaviors, help speed the pace of change, and improve performance over time. They include:

  - Develop a learning organization

  - Establish learning teams

  - Influence and recognize organizational change

  - Solve problems proactively

  - Identify true root cause

Some key aspects of an effective and positive quality and compliance culture are depicted in Figure 1.3 (this topic is thoroughly discussed in the following Chapter).

Organizational environment

- Positive, blame-free attitude toward errors and mistakes

- Commitment by top management to involving the workforce

- Low levels of job stress

- High levels of job satisfaction

Management systems

- Availability of resources

- Quality prioritized over production and profits

- Open two-way communications

- High quality of training

- Good ways of informing and consulting the workforce about quality

People

- Trust in workforce to manage quality

- Management commitment and leadership toward quality

- Cooperation between employees

- High level of workforce participation in quality

Behavior

- Recognition of the fact that everyone has a role to play

- Acceptance of personal responsibility for quality

- Frequent formal and informal communication about quality

Hardware

- Good plant design and maintenance and good working conditions

Figure 1.3 Aspects associated with an effective quality culture

1.3 Quality culture maturity attributes and models

Phillips Crosby's Quality Management Maturity Grid[10] was one of the first formal attempts to characterize the level of quality of an organization. Using his own words "if quality is to be a first among equals, then management must have a way of measuring and controlling". He envisioned the Grid to help managers to determine where the operations stands from a quality standpoint.

The Grid is divided into five stages of management maturity (Uncertainty, Awakening, Enlightenment, Wisdom, and Certainty), measured against six dimensions, to complete the matrix:

- Management understanding and attitude (towards quality management)

- Quality organization status

- Problem handling experience

- Cost of quality as a percentage of sales

- Quality improvement actions

- Summation of company quality posture

[10]Crosby, Phillip B. 1980. *Quality Is Free*. New York: Penguin Group

The FDA Quality Metrics Research 2019 report[11] presented the following definition of Quality Maturity:

Objective characteristics of a quality system that can be observed or verified upon inspection or internal audit and that have a positive relationship with quality culture behaviors, including formal programs in preventive maintenance, environmental health and safety, risk management, human error prevention, and training or continuous improvement.

This study identified ten attributes that most strongly differentiate sites in terms of their overall Quality Maturity implementation:

1. Optimized set-up and cleaning procedures are documented as best-practice process and rolled-out throughout the whole plant

2. A large percentage of equipment on the shop floor is currently under statistical process control (SPC)

3. For root cause analysis we have standardized tools to get a deeper understanding of the influencing factors (for example, DMAIC)

4. Goals and objectives of the manufacturing unit are closely linked and consistent with corporate objectives and the site has a clear focus

5. We have joint improvement programs with our suppliers to increase our performance

6. All potential bottleneck machines are identified and supplied with additional spare parts

7. For product and process transfers between different units or sites standardized procedures exist, which ensure a fast, stable and complied knowledge transfer

---

[11]University of St. Gallen. 2019. *FDA Quality Metrics Research 3rd Year Report December 2019.* Switzerland

8. Charts showing the current performance status (for example, current scrap-rates, current up-times and so on) are posted on the shop-floor and visible for everyone

9. We regularly survey our customer's requirements

10. We rank our suppliers; therefore, we conduct supplier qualifications and audits

Another interesting study is the **PDA's Quality Culture Survey report** published in 2015[12] which included five top quality attributes that can serve as surrogates for quality culture management communication that quality is everyone's responsibility:

1. Management communication that quality is everyone's responsibility

2. Site has formal quality improvement objectives and targets

3. Clear performance criteria for feedback and coaching

4. Quality topics included in at least half of all-hands meetings

5. Collecting error prevention metrics

These mature quality attributes are mainly related to management responsibility and continual improvement areas of the pharmaceutical quality system sections of ICH Q10, and therefore may be amenable to be incorporated in audit programs or in regulatory inspections.

Quality culture indicators (discussed in Chapter 4) enable companies to assess and characterize the level of implementation and maturity of their quality journey.

---

[12]Patel, Pritesh et al. 2015. "Quality Culture Survey Report." *PDA J. Pharm Sci and Tech*, 69: 631-642

Table 1.1 Comparison of the identified maturity attributes to the requirements of ICH Q10

Identified Maturity Attribute	ICH Q10
Management communication that Quality is Everyone's Responsibility	*Section 2.1* Management Commitment (a) Senior management has the ultimate responsibility to ensure an effective pharmaceutical quality system is in place to achieve the quality objectives, and that roles, responsibilities, and authorities are defined, communicated and implemented throughout the company
Site has formal quality improvement objectives and targets	*Section 2.2* Quality Policy and *2.3* Quality Planning
Clear performance criteria for feedback and coaching	*Section 2.4* Resource Management (a) Management should determine and provide adequate and appropriate resources (human, financial, materials, facilities and equipment) to implement and maintain the pharmaceutical quality system and continually improve its effectiveness (b) Management should ensure that resources are appropriately applied to a specific product, process or site
Quality topics included in at least half of all-hands meetings	*Section 2.5* Internal Communication (a) Management should ensure appropriate communication processes are established and implemented within the organization (b) Communications processes should ensure the flow of appropriate information between all levels of the company
Collecting error prevention metrics	*Section 4* Continual improvement of the pharmaceutical quality system

A wise recommendation is that companies should develop and implement their own maturity model using the leadership, people engagement and culture and maturity metrics described in Chapter 4. A simple three-level grid including *initial*, *intermediate*, and *advance* levels could be very useful to initiate this journey into developing and implementing a quality culture maturity model. I do not advocate for complex matrixes because companies can lose the focus of what is really important - to implement those indicators and to monitor their improvement. Remember that this is a long journey.

In October 2020, FDA's Center for Drug Evaluation and Research launched quality management maturity pilots for APIs and finished dosage forms. The objective of those pilot programs is to "gain insight from third-party assessments of a manufacturer's quality management system to inform future development of an FDA rating system," according to CDER's announcement to industry of the new pilot programs.[13]

One pilot program will characterize quality management maturity (QMM) for finished dosage forms from domestic manufacturers of prescription and over-the-counter (OTC) drug products. The second pilot will look at QMM for active pharmaceutical ingredients (APIs), including drug substance intermediates, from foreign manufacturers and destined for use in FDA-regulated prescription and OTC products.[14]

The agency established that "characteristics of a mature quality management system include, for example, the ability to consistently and reliably deliver quality product over time, operational stability, and a *strong quality culture*. Additionally, for manufacturers with a mature quality management system, FDA can exercise a more flexible regulatory approach, leading toward the goal of producing high-quality drug products without extensive regulatory oversight."

Some of the topics anticipated to be assessed in the pilot program, said FDA in the announcement, include:

- supply chain management

- manufacturing strategy and operations

---

[13]https://www.federalregister.gov/documents/2020/10/16/2020-22976/quality-management-maturity-for-finished-dosage-forms-pilot-program-for-domestic-drug-product, accessed 2/03/2021

[14]https://www.federalregister.gov/documents/2020/10/16/2020-22977/quality-management-maturity-for-active-pharmaceutical-ingredients-pilot-program-for-foreign, accessed 2/03/2021

- safety, environmental, and regulatory compliance

- inventory management

- performance management and continual improvement

- risk management

- management review and responsibility

- planning

- workforce management

- quality culture

- customer experience

Therefore, the implementation of a strong, positive quality culture within a pharmaceutical company is progressively becoming a necessity rather than a nice-to-have, voluntary program.

1.4 Behavior-based quality culture

Behavior-based management can be viewed as the system of management based on the sciences of human behavior and organizational culture, which is used by an organization to produce results. Principles of management people, aiming to shaping and influencing behavior and performance are complex. Moreover, they are rarely integrated into approaches for enhancing performance and into pharmaceutical quality system management practices. Quality Behavior can be defined as:

Behaviors observed at the site or organization that are associated with a strong quality culture in areas such as clear communication and transparency, commitment and engagement, technical excellence, and standardization of requirements.

We develop and manufacture medical products under a QMS, for example ICH Q10 for pharmaceutical and biopharmaceutical or ISO 13485 for medical devices. We do not name them as quality leadership system. And very probably, everyone reading this book appreciate that management and leadership are different. Managers oversee and optimize processes to deliver results. Leaders change (improve) those processes to deliver greater results. Companies need both, managers and leaders as they are both necessary to produce and deliver safe and effective medical products to patients worldwide. In order words, we need better quality system management and more quality and compliance culture leadership.

Table 1.2 depicts differences between traditional QMS versus behavior-based quality and compliance culture for medical product manufacturers.

Table 1.2 Comparison between typical QMS and behavior-based quality culture

Medical Products Quality Management System	Behavior-based Medical Products Quality and Compliance Culture
Focus on processes	Focus on process and people (human factors)
Primarily based on GMP	Based on CGMP, risk management, behavioral science, and organizational culture
Simplistic view of behavior change	Behavior change is complex
Linear cause and effect thinking	Systematic thinking
Develop a quality/CGMP program	Develop and sustain a quality and compliance culture

A QMS is defined as a formalized system that documents processes, procedures, and responsibilities for achieving quality policies and objectives. A QMS helps coordinate and direct an organization's activities to meet customer and regulatory requirements and improve its effectiveness and efficiency on a continuous basis.

In the case of the pharmaceutical industry, many of the quality systems elements correlate closely with the CGMP regulations. It is a very process-focused system and yes, well-defined processes and standards are critical, but they are not sufficient to guarantee that medical products are safe and effective. A behavior-based quality and compliance culture is process focused, but it is also people focused.

Traditional medical products' QMS are primarily based on meet CGMP requirements. Under a behavior-based quality and compliance culture, we know that this is not enough. We understand that achieving quality success requires not only an understanding of the CGMP, but of the behavioral sciences and organization culture too. This is the main difference between having a quality program (for example, one based on CGMP requirements) and having a culture of quality and compliance. Leaders must figure out a way to get employees at all levels of the organization to do the right things, not because they are being held accountable to them, but because they believe in and are committed to quality and compliance.

There was, and still is, an overemphasis on training and quality control activities, including inspections, to modify behaviors and achieve better results. This is largely based on the belief that the desired behavior change can be achieved by simply training employees and inspecting processes. Leaving aside the fact that most of training programs in our industry are ill-designed and rarely they include appropriate measurement of effectiveness. It should be recognized that both activities are important, but they are not enough to effectively change behaviors and achieve quality success. We must understand the complexity of behavior and analyze the cause of the performance problem (lack of skill, lack of motivation, ineffective work system, and so on) before proposing the right solution.

A vast majority of medical product manufacturers address specific issues in isolation or as individual components, not as a whole or complete system. This can be observed looking their CAPA programs and noticing the lack of true preventive action. They only have corrections and corrective actions, and they approach quality and quality issues with a sort of linear cause-and-effect thinking. This linear thinking is not adequate to address complex issues. When a company implement a behavior-based quality and culture compliance, they look into their problems as a whole, and they understand that there are multiple factors (including the soft ones related to personal and organizational behaviors) that affect performance. A very positive consequence of this systematic thinking is the shift from CAPA programs mostly correctives to ones where the systemic preventive actions are predominant.

Quality behaviors and quality culture maturity levels strongly correlates in the pharmaceutical industry as determined in the **University of St. Gallen's FDA Quality Metrics Research Report**. In this report, the most significant quality behaviors were:

- Employees continuously strive to reduce any kind of waste in every process

- Plant management is personally involved in improvement projects

- Use of documented operating procedures to standardize our processes

- Maintenance department focuses on assisting machine operators perform their own preventive maintenance

- Emphasis on good maintenance as a strategy for increasing quality and panning for compliance

  Other important quality behaviors identified in the report were:

- Manufacturing managers have a good understanding of how the corporate/divisional strategy is formed

- Vision, mission and strategy is broadly communicated and lived by our employees

- Continuously measure of the quality of processes

- Command and control is seen as the most effective leadership style rather that open culture (inverse)

- Continuously optimize the maintenance program based on dedicated failure analysis

The ISPE Cultural Excellence Report published in 2017 includes a set of 21 desired key behaviors that support the six dimensions of cultural excellence previously mentioned. It can be considered a behavior-based framework to understand, assess, and develop excellence in quality culture within organizations.

Leadership and vision

- We regularly hear from management an emphasis on quality topics and the importance of quality

- When we have quality issues in conflict with business issues, both aspects are always considered by management before making a decision

- Leaders regularly provide sufficient support and coaching to line workers to help them improve quality

- Leaders always model the desired behavior of "doing the right thing" on issues of quality

Mindset and attitudes

- All employees consistently see quality and compliance as a personal responsibility

- Employees have sufficient authority to make decisions and feel trusted to do their jobs well

- Employees regularly identify issues and proactively intervene to minimize any potential negative impact on quality and compliance

- Employees are not afraid to speak up, identify quality issues, or challenge the status quo for improved quality; they believe management will act on their suggestions

Gemba and shop floor engagement

- There are both formal and informal processes in place to ensure management regularly visits the shop floor to observe, assess, listen, and coach the employees, such as Gemba walks

- There is evidence to confirm that the desired quality behaviors are routinely practiced on a day-to-day basis, for example, through Gemba walks

- Opportunities for continuous improvements are routinely identified and implemented, as appropriate

Monitoring and measurement

- Quality metrics and goals are consistently designed and selected to promote/motivate desired quality behaviors

- Up-to-date quality metrics (right first-time figures, excellence targets on defects, rejects) are regularly posted and easily visible near each production/work area

- All workers can routinely explain what quality information is tracked and why and outline their role in the achievement of quality goals

Management oversight and reporting

- Quality goals and objectives are routinely established, linked, and aligned with organizational goals

- Management is regularly involved in reviewing and assessing product, process, and quality system performance

- The company's oversight and reporting capabilities are systematically applied to effectively manage external manufacturing performance within the supply chain

- Management regularly involves line workers in problem identification, problem solving, troubleshooting, and investigations

Cultural enablers

- Improvement opportunities and problems are acknowledged quickly, mistakes are formally reviewed, and company looks to share and learn from them

- Management enables employees at all levels within the organization to identify and communicate risks well across the organization

- We routinely recognize and celebrate both individual and group improvement achievements in performance quality

- Employees regularly receive training that effectively helps them ensure quality in their work fostering a learning organization

The PDA's 2014 Quality Culture Metrics Survey identified the following behaviors for management personnel and the rest of the employees associated to its seven quality culture characteristics:

Communication and transparency

- Actively listen and engage in two-way communication

- Encourage honest dialog

- Share information on product quality performance with employees and partners

- Proactive and transparent behavior with regulators

- Follow through

- Communicate on a needed basis

Commitment and engagement

- Review quality issues that include executive level and/or CEO level staff

- Putting patients ahead of everything else

- Put "quality is everyone's responsibility" in practice

Hold people accountable

- Establish training on proper business conduct with mechanisms with hotlines to promote reporting of issues

- Choose leaders who exemplify quality culture behaviors

Technical excellence

- Hire individuals with appropriate technical expertise for their role

- Eager to share knowledge and expertise to solve problems

- Promote individuals based on performance and technical expertise

- Facilitate participation in external technical conferences and workshops

- Adoption of a Quality by Design (QbD) mindset and approach

- Promotion and application of Process Analytical Technology (PAT)

Standardization of criteria or requirements

- Following proper business conduct programs with mechanisms to promote reporting of issues

- Implementation of continuous improvement programs that measure progress (for example, Baldrige, Six Sigma, Kaizen, performance Boards, Cost of Quality, and so on)

- Management system that has clear performance criteria

- Following clear and transparent governance processes

- Conducting internal survey measuring and providing feedback on company's quality culture

- Requirements are site specific and not standardized across the entire organization

Cross-Functional Vision

- Established company values that include quality

- Cross functional quality goals are established

- Program of risk management and preventive quality is followed

- Management promotes staff's understanding of their individual impact on quality and safety

- Product quality is not compromised during implementation of lean manufacturing or other process improvement efforts

- Quality is perceived as an enforcer to catch and rectify quality issues

Rewards and recognition

- Encouraging or rewarding "speaking up" regarding quality issues

- Providing timely feedback and coaching of job performance

- Offering non-monetary recognition to individuals who achieve or support quality goals

- There is no tendency to point fingers and to lay blame to others

- Offering financial incentives linked achieving to quality goals

- The incentive program supports a strong quality culture

Speak Up for Quality Culture

- Facilitating escalation of issues

- Promoting continuous improvement

- Questioning or challenging non-value added activities

- Taking personal or individual accountability

- Doing the right thing when no one is watching

- Telling what the boss needs to know not just what she/she wants to hear

The top five observed behaviors from this study were:

    a.   Leaders who exemplify quality culture behavior

    b.   Incentive program supports a strong quality culture

c. Timely feedback and coaching of job performance

d. Following clear and transparent governance processes

e. Adoption of a quality by design (QbD) mindset and approach

Chapter 3 describes a comprehensive set of behavioral criteria associated to a strong and positive quality and compliance culture. They are described in their desired states and can be used to determine the level of maturity of the quality culture by indicating specific behaviors with lagging maturity within a pharmaceutical organization.

This comprehensive behavior-based approach to improving quality and compliance culture gives leaders and senior managers a practical means to shape cultural performance and deliver enhanced quality outcomes.

1.5 Why quality culture matters

Culture is everything and it permeates the entire QMS and is an essential element of its effectiveness. Quality culture has a direct impact on many aspects of an organization, including performance. Low quality means high cost.

Another example of increasingly importance of this topic is that at the time of this writing, the technical committee in charge of the ISO 9000 series of standards currently is writing ISO 10010 – *Quality management – Guidance to evaluate and improve quality culture to drive sustained success.* Culture sets the organizational values and keeps people in the organization aligned to work effectively to achieve the organization's vision, mission, and goals.

While no medical product regulations currently incorporate explicit requirements for a quality culture, for a medical product manufacturing company, quality is a matter of life or death. If your diagnostic products give incorrect results, it can take multiple unnecessary and expensive tests to clarify the situation, the patient might receive unnecessary treatments, or the incorrect result can prevent a much necessary treatment (think of a false negative result to a cancer patient). If you are a drug or medical device manufacturer, contaminated medicines or unclean devices can cause harm and even death to your patients. So, quality always matter but, in our environment, it can directly affect the life of our customers and patients.

A pharmaceutical QMS founded on a robust quality and compliance culture will provide the key elements of assurance and oversight necessary for both manufacturing and quality control laboratory processes. Using the own FDA words[15]:

"The requirements of good manufacturing practice are underpinned by a central objective: to create a system of programs, policies, processes, and facilities that prevent errors and defects. Senior managers in the drug industry are responsible for the effectiveness of this system, which is known as the Pharmaceutical Quality System (PQS). A PQS is successful when it assures an ongoing state of control. In a healthy PQS, managers establish a vigilant quality culture in which timely action is taken to prevent risks to quality. Lifecycle adaptations are made to address manufacturing weaknesses and continually improve systems. An effective process performance and product quality monitoring program provides early warning of emerging quality issues. Systemic solutions are implemented rather than ineffective shortcuts. A firm will also habitually attend to the seemingly small problems that quality experts remind us later would accumulate into costly, complex problems. An effective PQS will ultimately support stable processes, and predictable quality and supply."

Legal framework within the U.S. Food, Drug and Cosmetic Act also addresses the requirement that senior managers/leaders must exert oversight and control to assure that medical products are safe and effective. For example:

501(a)(2)(B): A drug is adulterated if:
the methods used in, or facilities or controls used for, manufacturing, processing, packing, or holding do not conform with CGMP.

[15]https://www.fda.gov/drugs/pharmaceutical-quality-resources/quality-systems-drugs, accessed 2/03/2021

FDASIA §711: CGMP includes:

the implementation of quality oversight and controls over the manufacture of drugs, including the safety of raw materials, materials used in drug manufacturing, and finished drug products.

A strong and positive quality culture is a key component of operational excellence in the medical product industry. And more important, it is the road to achieve sustainable compliance in our industry. A strong, positive corporate quality culture will create manufacturing and quality product consistency, while a broken quality culture will nurture unreliable processes plagued with manufacturing and quality issues.

On the other hand, the symptoms of a broken quality culture within our industry have an enormous impact in the form of "cost of poor quality". It has a huge effect on performance, and it is probably the enemy number one in the list of situations jeopardizing the survival of medical product manufacturing companies.

Although culture in general and quality culture in particular are unique to every organization, we can identify some common threats creates by an inadequate or poor quality culture:

Internal failures

- Rework

- Rejected products

- Reinspection and retest

- Retraining

- Overwhelming investigations and CAPA programs

- Waterlogged and ineffective quality management systems

- Personnel overtime

- Premium freight costs

External failures

- Customer complaints

- Product recall

- Regulatory consequences

- Failing regulatory inspections

- Unsuccessful pre-approval inspection for new products

- Prohibition to sale products in certain market (import alerts in the case of U.S. FDA)

- Warning letter and untitled letter

- Vast remediation programs

- Independent third-party quality system certifications

- Regulatory meetings

- Revoke of product approval

- Criminal investigations

- Seizures

- Injunctions

- Consent decrees and disgorgements (huge fines and restitution costs)

- Debarment and disqualification Lists

1.6 Who creates and changes quality culture

Quality is everyone's responsibility, but when it comes to creating, strengthening, or maintaining a culture within an organization, there is one group who really own it, the leaders and senior managers.

As pointed by Schein "organizational culture is created by leaders, and one of the most decisive functions of leaderships may well be the creation, the management, and -if when necessary- the destruction of culture". Peter Drucker is quoted as saying "culture eats strategy for breakfast". Successful cultures are the vehicle to turn adequate strategies into stellar results.

The strength of any organization's quality culture is a direct reflection of how important quality and compliance is to its leadership. Quality culture starts at the top and flows downwards. It is a shared responsibility, but it is not created or changed from the bottom up.

Mid-level managers and supervisors are also considered leaders too. And they have a great responsibility to effectively advise senior leadership and influence upwards because they also own the culture.

Having a strong quality and compliance culture is a choice. Ideally, leaders of a company will choose to have a strong quality and compliance culture because it is the right thing to do. For medical product manufacturer companies, quality is not a priority, it is a critical-to-success value, a solid value of the organization.

Although less desirable, for other companies, establishing a strong quality culture might be motivated out of necessity. Their focus on improving their quality culture is reactionary and driven out by significant or major events such as product recall or regulatory authorities' interventions (consent decrees, import alert, failure to receive product approval, and so on).

Regardless of whether it is based on a proactive vision or a reactive event, creating a strong, positive quality and compliance culture does not happen by chance. Depending on the situations, changing the deep-rooted thoughts, beliefs and behaviors of a group can be difficult and take a long time.

The good news is that creating or strengthening a positive and sustainable quality culture is an achievable task although not an easy or quick one. Quality culture is a long journey but not a chimera. It requires five elements to be present:

Start with the top leadership - If top leaders are not actively engaged into the building of a strong quality and compliance culture, it will not work. CEO, Board of Directors, Chief Quality Officer, Chief Operations Officer, and so on must be leading the effort. Be supportive of it is not good enough nor sufficient. As Crosby said, support from top management is not sufficient. You need to start with an intentional commitment and hard work of leaders at all levels of the organization starting at the top.

Every employee must be involved - Require every employee to actively participate. The top-down deployment of the quality culture principles and required behaviors must reach every employee of the organization.

Build an internal network of quality coaches - Although this type of efforts typically begins with the support of external consultants, to be sustainable, the company must develop an internal group of quality coaches who maintain high the flame of a strong and positive quality culture.

Integrate quality and compliance metrics into performance management and hold management accountable - Every manager and leader need to become a quality advocate for the rest of the organization and more directly for their teams. Leading quality metrics, not just lagging ones, must be developed, and implemented as part of the performance management for every site. Every leader/manager must be hold accountable for the implementation and sustainability of the quality culture.

Transform your learning programs - Your existing learning programs and practices must be adapted to effectively incorporate the competencies and behaviors associated to an efficient quality and compliance culture.

Creating a culture of quality and compliance requires more that completing an annual employee survey and then leaving managers on their own, hoping they will be able to learn something from the survey results that will change how they manage.

1.7 How to change the quality culture – advice from the experts

This is a point where there is almost a full consensus: every leader knows that better quality and compliance has a direct impact in the bottom-line performance of the company. Changing the quality culture of an organization will also require a re-alignment and change to the general company's culture. Changing them is not an easy job but as Dr. Deming said: *It is not necessary to change. Survival is not mandatory.*

Changing the quality culture is attainable even in multicultural organizations if the top leadership make it their top priority.

The Gallup institute offered the following advice on what must happen to change a culture[16]:

> "Identify your purpose and brand. Top leaders must clearly identify your purpose -why you are in business- and how you want employees and customer to perceive your brand. Purpose and brand are the stage for everything else.
>
> Audit all programs and communications for alignment and consistence with your organization purpose and brand.
>
> Reposition your managers as coaches. Only your best managers can implement the culture you want. A great culture is one of the few things an organization cannot buy. Managers at all levels make or break your cultural change. Moving your managers from boss to coach not only increase employee engagement and improves performance, but it's also essential to changing your culture."

Recognition: create a culture of appreciation and positive reinforcement

Create a recognition program that promotes the positive cultural values and behaviors you want to see more of. Regardless of the kind of quality culture your organization has today or wants to have in the future, I cannot think of a negative impact of improving the amount of

---

[16]Clifton, Jim & Jim Harter. 2019. *It's the Manager.* New York: Gallup Press

recognition within your organization. Recognition encourages more of the same behaviors. We all need recognition and approval. It helps motivate us to do it all again. Section 2.9 covers in detail the use of consequences to increase or decrease behaviors.

Behavioral consequences are those things and events that follow a behavior and change the probability that the behavior will be repeated in the future. A significant part of every manager's job is to identify the behaviors that are necessary and sufficient to accomplish the company's objectives and then to arrange for consequences to support them.

Consequences that are immediate and certain are very powerful in governing behaviors. The immediacy factor explains the difference between a reinforcer and a reward. A small reinforcer provided immediately for a behavior has much more effect on that behaviors than a larger but delayed reward. As explained by Audrey C. Daniels in his book Bringing out the best in people – How to apply the astonishing power of positive reinforcement[17] "Compensation alone will not do the job of maximizing performance. Only effective and frequent positive reinforcement can do that".

Learning from the experts
The following pages are devoted to three of the most influential people in the field of Quality. Current quality culture philosophy is anchored in the pioneering ideas established by W. Edwards Deming, Phil B. Crosby, and Joseph M. Juran (with the collaboration of many others). Their ideas were published around 40 years ago but they are fully alive today.

Best effort not sufficient

Need for consistence of effort

Measures of productivity do not lead to improvement in productivity

Low quality means high costs

[17]Daniels, Aubrey C. 2016. *Bringing Out the Best in People*. 3rd ed. New York: McGraw Hill

Quality is made in the boardroom

Quality cannot be delegated – Quality is everyone's responsibility

Support of top management is not sufficient; action is required

"... and if you can't come, send nobody"

There is no substitute for Knowledge

Information is not Knowledge

*The responsibility of supervisors must be changed from
sheer numbers to quality*

*Quality must be built into the product,
and testing alone cannot be relied on to ensure product quality*

Figure 1.4 Deming's quotations

All the above phrases are from **Dr. W. Edwards Deming** one of the most important and influential thinkers for quality and management fields. In his seminal book published in 1982, *Out of Crisis*[18], he included a recipe of 14 points for management. Deming defined those 14 points are the basis for transformation of American industry. As he said "it will not suffice merely to solve problems, big or little. Adoption and action on the 14 points are a signal that the management intend to stay in business and aim to protect investors and jobs". The 14 points are practices that should be followed, and they constitute an effective road map to transform the quality culture of any organization.

Born in 1900, Deming was an American engineer, professor, statistician, lecturer, author, and management consultant. Deming opined that by embracing certain principles of the management, organizations can improve the quality of the product and concurrently reduce costs. Reduction of costs would include the reduction of waste production, reducing staff attrition and litigation while simultaneously

---

[18]Deming, William E.1982. Out of Crisis. Cambridge: MIT

increasing customer loyalty. The key, in Deming's opinion, was to practice constant improvement.

Applying the Deming's 14 points for management throughout the different organizational levels results in a complete transformation. By going through these 14 points in all layers of the organization, a complete transformation can be achieved.

Profound knowledge

Deming indicates that every company – large or small, serving or producing, profitable or non-profit – always deals with universal knowledge. Deming calls this profound knowledge, which penetrates a company from the outside. That leads to transformation, where the sitting management needs to be open to. According to Deming, the system of profound knowledge is made up of four components through which the world is looked at simultaneously. These components function as lenses through which we see, and all four are related to each other:

- Valuing the system

- The concept of variation and knowledge about this

- Psychology

- The theory of knowledge

Deming's 14 points for Management

With the 14 important management principles he offered a way to drastically improve the organization's effectiveness. Many of these management principles are philosophical in nature, and some are more programmatic. All Deming's 14 points for management can bring about transformation. Below is a short description of the 14 points:

1) *Create constancy of purpose* toward improvement of product and service, with the aim to become competitive and to stay in business, and to provide jobs.

2) *Adopt the new philosophy*. We are in a new economic age. Western management must awaken to the challenge, must learn their responsibilities, and take on leadership for change.

3) *Cease dependence on inspection to achieve quality.* Eliminate the need for inspection on a mass basis by building quality into the product in the first place.

4) *End the practice of awarding business on the basis of price tag.* Instead, minimize total cost. Move toward a single supplier for any one item, on a long-term relationship of loyalty and trust.

5) *Improve constantly and forever* the system of production and service, to improve quality and productivity, and thus constantly decrease costs.

6) *Institute training on the job.*

7) *Institute leadership*. The aim of supervision should be to help people and machines and gadgets to do a better job. Supervision of management is in need of overhaul, as well as supervision of production workers.

8) *Drive out fear,* so that everyone may work effectively for the company.

9) *Break down barriers between departments.* People in research, design, sales, and production must work as a team, to foresee problems of production and in use that may be encountered with the product or service.

10) *Eliminate slogans, exhortations and target* for the work force asking for zero defects and new levels of productivity. Such exhortations only create adversarial relationships, as the bulk of the causes of low quality and low productivity belong to the system and thus lie beyond the power of the work force.

11) A) *Eliminate work standards* (quotas) on the factory floor. Substitute leadership.

11) B) *Eliminate management by objective.* Eliminate management by numbers, numerical goals. Substitute leadership.

12 A) *Remove barriers* that rob the hourly worker of his right to pride of workmanship. The responsibility of supervisors must be changed from sheer numbers to quality.

12 B) *Remove barriers that rob people in management and in engineering of their right to pride of workmanship.* This means, inter alia, abolishment of the annual or merit rating and of management by objective.

13 *Institute a vigorous program of education and self-improvement.*

14 *Put everybody in the company to work to accomplish the transformation.* The transformation is everybody's job.

Transformation

By being open to change, an organization opens itself to transformation. The first step is the transformation of the individual, every employee separately. This transformation does not take place at the same pace for everyone. For some it goes quicker than for others.

When the individual employee opens himself up for transformation, he can experience new meaning in his life regarding events, figures and deadlines and interactions between people. Therefore, he will apply his principles in any form of relationship with other people. He will lay the foundation for evaluating his own choices and how he can apply this in the organization where he works.

As a result, he is able to act as an example, listen well to others and constantly listen and learn from others. When all employees transform in this way, the entire organization will transform and apply a new philosophy according to Deming's 14 points for management.

Deming also outlined **Seven Deadly Diseases**, which describe the most serious barriers that management potentially faces within an organization. Outlined below are the **Seven Deadly Diseases of Management,** as well as an explanation of each:

1. **Lack of constancy of purpose** to plan product and service that will have a market and keep the company in business and provide   jobs.
    As long as the focus is on short term thinking, management will fail to plan adequately. Without good long-term planning, worker efforts will be irrelevant: Total Quality Management (TQM) cannot be a fad, as long-term forward progress should always be the ultimate goal for any organization.

2. **Emphasis on short-term profits**. Short-term thinking - the opposite of constancy of purpose - in order to stay in business, fed by fear of the push from bankers and owners for dividends. Boosting short-term profits is easier, at it typically involves the cutting of any expense related to the long term: training, quality assurance management, maintenance, and so on.

3. **Personal review systems**, or evaluation of performance, merit rating, annual review, etc. for people in management, the effects of which are devastating. Management by objective, on a go / no-go basis, without a method for accomplishment of the objective, is the same thing as management by fear. The essential problem with merit systems is that they reward results rather than process improvement-results will almost always have a lot of system luck mixed in. Some managers want to reward people who cooperate more or who seem to have better attitudes and will insist that they can recognize the people who are most cooperative and have the highest work ethic. Instead, managers should understand that the best way to develop cooperation is by focusing on the nature of work environment, not monetary rewards.

4. **Mobility of management: job-hopping.** The simplest and yet one of the deadliest of quality systems management diseases, management mobility (or when top management changes organizations every 3-4 years) means continuous improvement efforts will be broken and disjointed as new leaders come on board. With changes in leadership, there is a change in management philosophy. Managers who have an eye on the next

promotion want results - now - to gain the next rung on the ladder.

5. **Use of visible figures only for management**, with little or no consideration of figures that are unknown or unknowable. Some facts are simply unknowable. Knowing this, Deming insisted that leaders must still make decisions and manage a situation. This leads to a basic dilemma-how do you know what would have happened if you had kept on your prior course? How do you put a dollar value on the customer loyalty won through quality improvement efforts? You cannot, because these numbers are unknowable-and this must be taken into consideration.

6. **Excessive medical costs.** For the economy, health care as a percentage of overall expenditures has steadily risen for decades, which gradually pushes numerous businesses into a state of crisis. Potentially the only remedy for this disease would be a political system attempting to reform health care.

7. **Excessive costs of liability**. Deming blamed America's lawyers in part for the problems of American business. The U.S. has more lawyers per capita than any other country in the world, and they spend much of their professional time finding people to sue. Like health care costs in No. 6, Deming believed the remedy to this disease will probably have to come from the government.

Philips B. Crosby
Below are some famous quotes from Phil Crosby:

Improving quality requires a culture change, not just a new diet.

In a true zero-defects approach, there are no unimportant items

It is always cheaper to do the job right the first time

*Making a wrong decision is understandable. Refusing to search
continually for learning is not*

Quality has to be caused, not controlled

*Quality is free. It's not a gift, but it's free.
The"unquality" things are what cost money*

*Quality is such an attractive banner that sometimes we think
we can get away with just waving it, without doing the
hard work necessary to achieve it*

*Quality is the result of a carefully constructed cultural
environment
It has to be the fabric of the organization, not part of the fabric.*

Figure 1.5 Crosby's quotations

Born in 1926, Philips B. Crosby was an author and businessman who contributed to management theory and quality management practices.

Crosby's principle, *Doing It Right the First Time*, was his answer to the quality crisis. He defined quality as full and perfect conformance to the customers' requirements. The essence of his philosophy is expressed in what he called the Absolutes of Quality Management and the Basic Elements of Improvement.

The Absolutes of Quality Management

Crosby defined Four Absolutes of Quality Management, which are:

1. The First Absolute: The definition of quality is conformance to requirements

2. The Next Absolute: The system of quality is prevention

3. The Third Absolute: The performance standard is zero defects

4. The Final Absolute: The measurement of quality is the price of non-conformance

Crosby's **Zero Defects** is a performance method and standard that states that people should commit themselves to closely monitoring details and avoid errors. By doing this, they move closer to the zero defects goal. According to Crosby, zero defects was not just a manufacturing principle but was an all-pervading philosophy that ought to influence every decision that we make. Managerial notions of defects being unacceptable and everyone doing "things right the first time" are reinforced.

The Fourteen Steps to Quality Improvement

1. *Management Commitment* - Make it clear that management is committed to quality

2. *Quality Improvement Teams* - Form Quality Improvement Teams with senior representatives from each department

3. *Measure Processes* - Measure processes to determine where current and potential quality problems lie

4. *Cost of Quality* - Evaluate the cost of quality and explain its use as a management tool

5. *Quality Awareness* - Raise the quality awareness and personal concern of all employees

6. *Correct Problems* - Take actions to correct problems identified through previous steps

7. *Monitor Progress* - Establish progress monitoring for the improvement process

8. *Train Supervisors* - Train supervisors to actively carry out their part of the quality improvement program

9. *Zero Defects Day* - Hold a Zero Defects Day to reaffirm management commitment

10. *Establish Improvement Goals* - Encourage individuals to establish improvement goals for themselves and their group

11. *Remove Fear* - Encourage employees to tell management about obstacles to improve quality

12. *Recognize* - Recognize and appreciate those who participate

13. *Quality Councils* - Establish Quality Councils to communicate on a regular basis

14. *Repeat the Cycle* - Do it all over again to emphasize that the quality improvement process never ends

The Quality Vaccine

Crosby explained that this vaccination was the medicine for organizations to prevent poor quality. It consists of:

a. **Integrity:** Quality must be taken seriously throughout the entire organization, from the highest levels to the lowest. The company's future will be judged by the quality it delivers.

b. **Systems**: The right measures and systems are necessary for quality costs, performance, education, improvement, review, and customer satisfaction.

c. **Communication:** Communication is a very important factor in an organization. It is required to communicate the specifications, requirements, and improvement opportunities of the organization. Listening to customers and operatives intently and incorporating feedback will give the organization an edge over the competition.

d. **Operations:** a culture of improvement should be the norm in any organization, and the process should be solid.

e. **Policies:** policies that are implemented should be consistent and clear throughout the organization.

Joseph M. Juran[19]

...every successful quality revolution has included the participation of upper management. We know of no exceptions

For many phenomena, 80% of consequences stem from 20% of the causes

Without a standard there is no logical basis for making a decision or taking action

Goal setting has traditionally been based on past performance. This practice has tended to perpetuate the sins of the past

All improvement happens project by project and in no other way

Figure 1.6 Juran's quotations

Born in 1904, Josep M. Juran was a Romanian-born American engineer and management consultant of the 20th century, and a missionary for quality and quality management. Like Deming, Juran's philosophy also took root in Japan. He stressed on the importance of a broad, organizational-level approach to quality – stating that total quality management begins from the highest position in the management and continues all the way to the bottom.

Influence of the Pareto Principle
In 1941, Juran was introduced to the work of Vilfredo Pareto. He studied the Pareto principle (the 80-20 law), which states that, for many events, roughly 80% of the effects follow from 20% of the causes and applied the concept to quality issues. Thus, according to Juran, 80% of the problems in an organization are caused by 20% of the causes. This is also known as the rule of the "Vital Few and the Trivial Many". Juran, in his later years, preferred "the Vital Few and the Useful Many"

[19]Juran, Joseph M. 1989. *Juran on Leadership for Quality. An Executive Handbook.* New York: The Free Press

suggesting that the remaining 80% of the causes must not be completely ignored.

What was Juran's Philosophy?

The primary focus of every business, during Juran's time, was the quality of the end product, which is what Deming stressed upon. Juran shifted track to focus instead on the human dimension of quality management. He laid emphasis on the importance of educating and training managers. For Juran, the root cause of quality issues was the resistance to change, and human relations problems.

His approach to quality management drew one outside the walls of a factory and into the non-manufacturing processes of the organization, especially those that were service-related.

The Juran Quality Trilogy

Juran was one of the first to write about the cost of poor quality, Juran developed an approach for cross-functional management that comprises three processes:

1. **Quality Planning**: This is a process that involves creating awareness of the necessity to improve, setting certain goals and planning ways to reach those goals. This process has its roots in the management's commitment to planned change that requires trained and qualified staff.

2. **Quality Control**: This is a process to develop the methods to test the products for their quality. Deviation from the standard will require change and improvement.

3. **Quality Improvement**: This is a process that involves the constant drive to perfection. Quality improvements need to be continuously introduced. Problems must be diagnosed to the root causes to develop solutions. The management must analyze the processes and the systems and report back with recognition and praise when things are done right.

Juran also introduced the **Three Basic Steps to Progress**, which, in his opinion, companies must implement if they are to achieve high quality:

1. Accomplish improvements that are structured on a regular basis with commitment and a sense of urgency

2. Build an extensive training program

3. Cultivate commitment and leadership at the higher ranks of management

Ten Steps to Quality

Juran devised ten steps for organizations to follow to attain better quality.

1. Establish awareness for the need to improve and the opportunities for improvement

2. Set goals for improvement

3. Organize to meet the goals that have been set

4. Provide training

5. Implement projects aimed at solving problems

6. Report progress

7. Give recognition

8. Communicate results

9. Keep score

10. Maintain momentum by building improvement into the company's regular systems

1.8 Signs of a weak culture of quality

Many organizations only reach up to the level of developing and implementing (with more or less success) a quality program, based mainly on reactive activities such as inspection and testing. Their measurement of the quality system performance is based on reactive, lagging metrics This cannot be confused with having an effective quality culture as defined previously in this Chapter. A culture of quality helps organizations achieve their quality goals. With any doubt, one of the most striking indicators of a weak culture is the lack of leadership.

The following is an incomplete list of some of the most important signs of a weak culture of quality and compliance:

- Lack of leadership emphasis on quality. Senior executives rarely discuss quality, let alone performance against quality objectives.

- Leadership and management in general share a lack of adequate quality and regulatory knowledge and education.

- The organization's quality vision is either non-existent or has minimal linkage to business strategy.

- Lack of message credibility - managers throughout the organization either fail to consistently emphasize quality or are resistant to quality initiatives.

- The organization has few if any feedback loops for continuous improvement of processes.

- The organization lacks formal mechanisms for collecting and analyzing customers (both internal and external) feedback, including measuring employees' perception about the culture of quality of the organization.

- Metrics used for performance evaluation feature little-to-no mention of quality goals.

- Lack of employees' engagement. No ownership and empowerment. Employees are not familiar with the organization's quality vision and values, or perhaps worse, view them as mere slogans.

- Poor training and development programs lacking emphasis on quality. In our industry, this translates into lack of basic compliance education, lack of understanding of CGMP, and lack of understanding of human factors affecting performance and quality.

- New hires are not formally introduced to the organization's quality vision and values. New hires in our industry typically received insufficient onboarding training specially in the area of CGMP and compliance.

- The organization experiences frequent setbacks owing to inconsistent quality.

- Risk management processes are mainly used to justify substandard product quality rather than as a proactive, preventive tool to enhance quality of products and compliance of quality system processes.

- Lack of accuracy managing and reporting quality data, even as part of regulatory submissions, which constitute both a data integrity issue and careless work.

- Fear and retaliation management style using mostly only negative consequences.

- Leadership never take responsibility for quality and regulatory mishaps. Enforcement is seeming as regulatory persecutions and retaliations rather than lack adequate quality culture and management oversight.

- Lack of trust – management has no confidence on workers and workers have no confidence on management actions neither.

- Management reviews only include lagging indicators/metrics. No proactive, leading indicators are evaluated.

- Missed commitments is another clear sign of a poor-quality culture and lack of leadership and management oversight. It ranges from overdue CGMP reports (investigations, CAPA, complaint investigations, and so on) to overdue remediation commitments made to regulatory authorities. When you commit with regulatory authorities to complete an action or to send a report by a certain date, even though you called it a "target" day, for regulators it becomes a "no later than" date. Obviously, specific circumstances may well justify a delay of such commitment, but it should be the exception, not the norm.

- Lack of enough competent personnel, including the quality organization. Under a robust quality system, sufficient resources should be allocated for effective and efficient operational activities. Senior management is responsible for providing adequate resources which is key to creating a robust quality system and complying with the CGMP regulations. Although quality unit personnel should not take on the responsibilities of other units of the organization, these personnel should be selected based on their scientific and technical understanding, product knowledge, process knowledge and/or risk assessment abilities to appropriately execute quality functions. Past due or constant extensions of due dates for CGMP documents (change controls, investigations, CAPAs, and so on) is just a symptom of this lack of enough personnel.

- Lack of leadership oversight and control of regulatory remediation activities. Hire and pay remediation consultants is not enough. Leaders are themselves responsible for the remediation, from selecting the adequate consultants to constantly oversight them. Leaders cannot delegate this responsibility to the consultants.

Finally, I'd like to briefly describe perhaps the most dangerous and vicious enemy of a strong, positive culture of quality and compliance - the *nano-manager* which can also be named as the *anti-culture* manager. Everyone knows examples of leaders who require to be copied in all emails, and that want to be part of all decisions, including many technical decisions out of his knowledge and capabilities. And then, they do not read and act on those communications. I know one of these cases where he did not read nor answer a critical request of information by the U.S. FDA (before an inspection) for 6 months.

1.9 The House of Quality

In the following Chapters, readers will find the foundational principles and values of a strong, positive quality culture (Chapter 2), and the three basic pillars needed to build an effective QMS: a) enough competent people (Chapter 5), b) an adequate training and development program (Chapter 6), and c) adequate documentation (Chapter 7) including procedures, work instruction, and so on. All those elements together shape our house of quality as depicts in Figure 1.7.

An effective and efficient quality system must be built on a solid quality and compliance culture foundation which, in turns, need also a very solid foundation. The foundation of any company is its values and principles and to be successful and build an effective quality culture the company must define culture as a foundational and core principle.

Values and principles are not the same than priorities. Priorities can change depending on circumstances, but values/principles should not. In organizations with strong cultures (either safety, service, quality, and so on) current or past leaders have formulated a set of core values that became their guiding principles. Most of the time they document those principles as a commitment or credo. Documenting commitments in writing is an important element an effective culture because by doing so, leaders are increasing the pressure for the actions of the employees (including leaders) to be consistent with its beliefs.

When creating a quality and compliance culture, this is a good place to start. Why most organizations fail? Because their actions are no aligned with those writing principles that very often fill entrance halls and corridors all over building walls. And the reasons for failures are several, beginning with the leadership failing to follow such commitments.

Figure 1.7 House of quality

Chapter 2
Quality Culture Principles

N ot much has been written and investigated about quality culture so far but we have the benefits of very good investigations and studies related to safety culture. In my consulting career, I often use as benchmark the successful implementation of safety culture by many companies. More often that one will expect, we are assisting manufacturing sites plagued with serious quality issues but with a good record in terms of safety issues. Invariably, the cause is that the company has a strong safety culture.

Continuing with this benchmark process with safety culture, there is a remarkable study titled *Driving Toward "0" Best Practices in Corporate Safety and Health* by Meredith Armstrong Whiting and Charles J. Bennett[20] where they found that the safety culture of 65 leading U.S. companies had similar core principles. Although the report focuses on occupational health and safety issues, their findings are widely applicable, including to the journey towards an effective quality culture. If safety is not prioritized as part of the organizational culture, then unsafe behaviors are more likely to occur. The same reasoning principle does apply to quality: if quality is not prioritized over production goals, for example, then corner-cutting behaviors will emerge.

---

[20]https://www.osha.gov/dcsp/compliance_assistance/conf_board_report_2 003.pdf, accessed 2/03/2021

Companies striving for outstanding quality marks are not only ensuring strict regulatory compliance, but they are also developing their own best practices to enhance their performance. The primary drivers are:

- A strong belief that poor quality (rejections, rework, reinspection, process deviations, customer complaints, and so on) is unacceptable in their operations

- A firm conviction that business benefits – directly, through reduced costs, and indirectly, through improve morale and increased productivity

- Confidence on the part of all employees that the company values quality comparably with other values, and an understanding by all employees of how to achieve the expected performance

- Everyone is committed and engaged

- Line workers gain confidence in the organization by observing the behavior of leaders and management at all levels

- Managers win the confidence of employees through a variety of means, including walking around (Gemba walks) and listening to workers' concerns, supporting and participating in the internal audit programs, and acting as role models

Medical product manufacturing companies are highly regulated (in the case of the U.S. by the Food and Drug Administration, FDA) and global companies must deal with multiples regulations. However, it is crucial to understand that regulations (for example, U.S. FDA's current Good Manufacturing Practices or CGMPs), represent only minimum requirements. Regulators, and more important, our patients and customers, expect that we implement comprehensive, modern quality systems and risk management approaches that exceed those minimum standards. Just meeting the CGMPs and other regulations is insufficient.

Many medical product manufacturing companies still believe that quality problems are created by the "plague of human error" as one vice-president of operational excellence once described it to me. My opinion, based on direct knowledge of the CAPA systems of some of the biggest regulated companies in the world, is that no one has been successful in reducing the "plague" to a controlled stage. The so-called human errors continue to be an epidemic for regulated companies. This lack of success comes despite some companies undertaking huge investment in technology, for example, making more graphical and pictorial procedures with many color images, better formatted manufacturing records, and so on.

It is necessary to remark that quality problems cannot be eliminated, nor even significantly reduced, simply by telling the person who made the error or mistake to be more careful. A general admonition or advisory to stop such behavior is a very simplistic approach and it does not work because we are not addressing any root cause. Quality problems will not disappear by simply disciplining the people who make the mistakes.

Their lack of success come from a single factor: *they are not changing the quality culture*, starting from the top of the organization. Some of the required changes include:

- Promoting quality of processes over yield of processes

- Promoting and requiring personal accountability at all levels

- Using risk management tools to avoid nonconformances, not to justify the acceptability of using nonconforming products

In general, we can find some common characteristics shared by companies with a strong, positive quality and compliance culture:

- Clearly describe what people are expected to do for quality

- Make quality a line management responsibility and accountability

- Incorporate quality into the business process as an operational strategy

- Use proactive quality and compliance measurements

- Have top leaders <u>do not</u> support quality, they <u>must</u> lead it

The rest of this Chapter discusses the ten principles representing the foundational values of a strong quality culture for medical product manufacturing companies. One of the definitions of a "principle" is that it is a basic belief, theory or rule that has a major influence on the way in which something is done.

Quality culture principles are a set of fundamental beliefs, norms, rules and values that are accepted as true and can be used as a basis to create and sustain a strong, positive culture towards quality and compliance. These principles are not listed in priority order. The relative importance of each principle will vary from company to company and can be expected to change over time.

These ten principles are:

1. Leadership at the top

2. Clear management visibility and leadership

3. Accountability and engagement to all levels: acceptance of personal responsibility for quality

4. Sharing of knowledge and information

5. Robust decision making and scientific, system-based approach to compliance

6. Creating quality and compliance performance expectations

7. Educating and training to influence behavior; continually developing people's skills and knowledge

8. Developing quality and compliance goals and metrics

9. Using consequences to increase or decrease behaviors

10. Commitment to resilience: learn from errors

ISO introduces in 2015[21] *seven quality management principles* which are the base for ISO 9000, ISO 9001 and related ISO quality management standards. In section 1.4, we discussed that medical products companies need to evolve from a quality management system to a behavior-based quality and compliance culture, and therefore, these seven quality management principles are strongly related to the quality culture principles previously described.

ISO's quality management principles are:

1. **Customer focus:** the primary focus of quality management is to meet customer requirements and to strive to exceed customer expectations.

2. **Leadership:** leaders at all levels establish unity of purpose and direction to create conditions in which people are engaged in achieving the company's quality objectives.

3. **Engagement of people:** competent, empowered and engaged people at all levels throughout the organization are essential to enhance its capability to create and deliver value.

4. **Process approach:** consistent and predictable results are achieved more effectively and efficiently when activities are understood and managed as interrelated process and function as a coherent system.

5. **Improvement**: successful organizations have an ongoing focus on improvement.

---

[21]https://www.iso.org/files/live/sites/isoorg/files/store/en/PUB100080.pdf, accessed 10/18/2020

6. **Evidence-based decision making:** decisions based on the analysis and evaluation of data and information are more likely to produce desired results.

7. **Relationship management:** for sustained success, an organization manages its relationships with interested parties, such as suppliers.

This Chapter provides a general perspective of the quality culture principles underlying an effective behavior-based medical products quality and compliance culture. It gives an overview of these principles and show how, collectively, they can form a basis for *create* and *sustain* cultural excellence and compliance.

There are many ways of applying these quality culture principles. The specific challenges a company faces will determine how to implement them.

For each of the ten principles which are the foundation of the quality culture presented in the following pages, we include a description and rationale for each principle, and the characteristics of a positive quality culture associated to it.

Behaviors to promote and leading quality indicators associated to each of the ten principles are described in Chapters 3 and 4, respectively.

Appendix A describes in a tabular form, the characteristics, desired behaviors, and leading indicators (metrics) that are be associated to each of the ten principles of a positive, strong quality and compliance culture.

2.1 Leadership at the top

Quality culture starts at the top and flows downward. It does not flow the bottom up. It is a leadership function to create a quality vision, set expectations, and inspire others to follow. Leaders at all levels establish unity of purpose and direction and create conditions in which people are engaged in achieving the company's quality objectives.

Curiously, we spoke about quality management systems, not about quality leadership systems. However, management and leadership are not the same thing. As explained by Maxwell (1988) "the main difference between the two is that leadership is about influencing people to follow, while management focuses on maintaining system and processes."

However, leadership and management must go hand in hand. They are not the same thing. But they are linked and complementary. Any effort to separate the two is likely to cause more problems than it solves.

Leaders define objectives and designate resources, and they act in a more strategic role. Managers organize resources to achieve a result by engaging the people in the organization, and they act in a more tactical role. Managers coordinate activities to direct and control an organization.

Leadership is the process for determining a possible future state that does not yet exist. Management is the coordinated activities to direct and control an organization. For an organization to succeed, it is imperative that it has both effective leadership and management.

Still, much ink has been spent delineating the differences. The manager's job is to plan, organize and coordinate. The leader's job is to inspire and motivate. In his 1989 book *On Becoming a Leader* Warren Bennis composed a list of the differences:

Table 2.1 Differences between a leader and a manager

- The manager administers; the leader innovates

- The manager maintains; the leader develops

- The manager focuses on systems and structure; the leader focuses on people

- The manager relies on control; the leader inspires trust

- The manager has a short-range view; the leader has a long-range perspective

- The manager asks how and when; the leader asks what and why

- The manager has his or her eye always on the bottom line; the leader's eye is on the horizon

- The manager imitates; the leader originates

- The manager accepts the status quo; the leader challenges it

- The manager does things right; the leader does the right thing

But in the current economy, where value comes increasingly from the knowledge of people, and where workers are no longer undifferentiated parts in an industrial machine, management and leadership are not easily separated. People look to their managers, not just to assign them a task, but to define for them a purpose. And managers must organize workers, not just to maximize efficiency, but to nurture skills, develop talent and inspire results. They must be more coaches than traditional managers.

The late management guru Peter Drucker was one of the first to recognize this truth. He identified the emergence of the "knowledge worker," and the profound differences that would cause in the way business was organized. With the rise of the knowledge worker, "one does not 'manage' people," Drucker wrote. "The task is to lead people. And the goal is to make productive the specific strengths and knowledge of every individual." Using a famous Drucker's quote "Management is doing things right; leadership is doing the right things". He also recommended that leaders must answer the following five questions which are further expanded in Chapter 8:

1. What is our mission?

2. Who is our customer?

3. What does the customer value?

4. What are our results?

5. What is our plan?

If top executives believe in the worth of the strategies, sets expectations for other managers, follows through on those expectations, and commits appropriate resources, shared beliefs, norms, and practices will evolve. All level of management, from the CEO to supervisors or team leaders, must live quality.

Focusing in the pharmaceutical/medical products manufacturing industry, the U.S. FDA established in the seminal 2006 Guidance for Industry *Quality Systems Approach to Pharmaceutical CGMP Regulations*, that "modern robust quality systems models call for management to play a key role in the design, implementation, and management of the quality system. Management is responsible for establishing the quality system structure appropriate for the specific organization and management has ultimate responsibility to provide the leadership needed for the successful functioning of a quality system."

In a robust, modern quality system, senior management should demonstrate commitment to developing and maintaining their quality system. Quality system plans should be aligned with a manufacturer's strategic plans to ensure that the system is part of the manufacturer's mission and quality strategies.

Senior managers set implementation priorities and develop action plans. When designing a robust quality system, management has the responsibility to structure the organization and ensure that assigned authorities and responsibilities support the production, quality, and management activities needed to produce quality products. Senior managers have the responsibility to ensure that the organization's structure is documented.

Implementing a robust quality and compliance culture can help ensure compliance with CGMP regulations related to drug safety, identity, strength, quality, and purity. Under the quality systems model, the Agency recommends that senior managers ensure that the quality system that is designed and implemented provides clear organizational guidance and facilitates systematic evaluation of issues.

Policies, objectives, and plans under a modern quality system provide the means by which senior managers articulate their vision of and commitment to quality to all levels of the organization.

Under a quality system, senior management should incorporate a strong commitment to quality into the organizational mission. Senior managers should develop an organizational quality policy that aligns with this mission; commit to meeting requirements and improving the quality system; and propose objectives to fulfill the quality policy. Under a quality system, to make the policy relevant, it must be communicated to, and understood by all personnel and revised, as needed.

Senior managers operating within a quality system should define the quality objectives identified for implementing the quality policy. Senior management should ensure that the quality objectives are created at the top level of the organization (and other levels as needed) through a formal quality planning process. Objectives are typically aligned with the manufacturer's strategic plans. A quality system seeks to ensure that managers support the objectives with necessary resources and have measurable goals that are monitored regularly.

Under a quality systems approach, managers would use quality planning to identify and allocate resources and define methods to achieve the quality objectives. Quality system plans should be documented and communicated to personnel to ensure awareness of how their operational activities are aligned with strategic and quality goals.

As a summary, senior management/leadership must ensure:

- Have top leaders lead quality

- Clearly visible, engaged, and unwavering senior management support for quality initiatives

- Leadership and vision

- Leaders at all level establish unit of purpose and direction and create conditions in which people are engaged in achieving the company's quality objectives

I would like to end the discussion of this key principle mentioning Dr. Deming. Out of his prolific writing about leadership as the engine of quality culture, following are three topics from his *Out of The Crisis* book:

Hope for instant pudding. An important obstacle is the supposition that improvement of quality and productivity is accomplished suddenly by affirmation of faith. Letters and telephone calls received by this author disclose prevalence of the supposition that one or two consultations with a competent consultant will set the company on the road to quality and productivity – instant pudding.

The supposition that is only necessary to meet specifications. There is obviously something wrong when a measured characteristic barely inside a specification is declared to be conforming; outside it is declared to be nonconforming. The supposition that everything is all right inside the specifications and all wrong outside does not correspond to this world.

A better description of the world is the Taguchi loss function in which there is minimum loss at the nominal value, and an ever-increasing loss with departure either way from the nominal value.

Survival of the fittest. Who will survive? Companies that adopt constancy of purpose for quality, productivity, and service, and go about it with intelligence and perseverance, have a chance to survive. They must, of course, offer products and services that have a market. Charles Darwin's law of survival of the fittest, and that the unfit do not survive, holds in free enterprise as well as in natural selection. It is a cruel law, unrelenting. Actually, the problem will solve itself. The only survivors will be companies with constancy of purpose for quality, productivity, and service.

2.2 Clear management visibility and leadership

To create a sustainable quality culture, leaders will need full buy-in and support from mid-level management. Employees at all levels must be sure that the organization values quality and compliance as one of its core values.

Managers at all level of the organization must (visibly) demonstrate their commitment to quality in everything they do and say. All employees in a power position must be role models for the other employees, and specially for the floor-line worker. The only way to gain employee confidence is for the leaders to walk the talk. Only if leaders, managers, and supervisors demonstrate a positive attitude towards quality and compliance, the employees will more likely do the same. If the employees perceive any inconsistences or compromises concerning the organization's commitment to quality, they will lose trust. Without trust, an organization or leader is no longer credible and unlikely to be followed.

However, be aware that adequate attitude toward quality is not enough, leaders must also develop their people and provide knowledge (see section 2.7) to enhance their competencies, especially those related to quality and compliance in our highly regulated industry.

A quality and compliance culture cannot be sustainably implemented until every member of the organization becomes a quality advocate. We should take advantage of the kind of products we make and the impact of those medical products in our society. The pacemaker you are making or the cancer drug you test can be used by a member of your family. I believe that there will be difficult to find a stronger motivator to do the right things right.

In our highly regulated manufacturing environment, all levels of management should provide support of the quality system by:

- Actively participating in system design, implementation, and monitoring, including system review (management reviews)

- Advocating continual improvement of operations of the quality system, and

- Committing necessary and adequate resources

In a robust quality systems environment, all managers should demonstrate strong and visible support for the quality system and ensure its implementation throughout the organization (for example, across multiple sites).

All managers should encourage internal communication on quality issues at all levels in the organization. Communication should be ongoing among research and development, regulatory affairs, manufacturing, and quality personnel on issues that affect quality, with top management included whenever appropriate.

All managers have the responsibility to communicate employee roles, responsibilities, and authorities within the QMS and ensure that interactions are defined and understood.

An organization also has the responsibility to give the individual who is appointed to manage the QMS the authority to detect problems and implement solutions.

A fundamental and key component in a robust quality culture is the quality system review. Senior managers should conduct reviews of the quality system's performance according to a planned schedule to ensure its continuing suitability, adequacy, and effectiveness. This review should include assessments of the process, product, and customer needs using both leading and lagging quality indicators. Under a quality systems approach, a review should consider at least the following:

- The appropriateness of the quality policy and objectives

- The results of audits and other assessments

- Customer feedback, including complaints

- The analysis of data trending results

- The status of actions to prevent a potential problem or a recurrence

- Any follow-up actions from previous management reviews

- Any changes in business practices or environment that may affect the quality system (such as the volume or type of operations)

- Product characteristics meeting the customer's needs

When developing and implementing new quality systems, reviews should take place more frequently than when the system has matured. Outside of scheduled reviews, the quality system should typically be included as a standing agenda item in general management meetings. In addition, a periodic review performed by a qualified source, external to the organization, may also be useful in assessing the suitability and effectiveness of the system.

Management oversight and review practices that engage both management and employees support a healthy quality culture because they demonstrate transparency, facilitate dialogue, bring attention to issues so they can be addressed, and highlight best practices so they can be replicated. Adequate management oversight and control of the QMS is one of the primary responsibilities of leaders and senior managers.

Management presence and engagement on the floor is a powerful way to demonstrate quality commitment to all members of the organization and to clear management visibility and leadership. Gemba walks allow site leaders to communicate clear messages using open and honest dialogue and provide a real indication of progress toward desired behaviors at all levels. Gemba walks also empower front-line employees by recognizing their contributions to site results and involving them in problem-solving and continuous improvement.

2.3 Accountability and engagement to all level: acceptance of personal responsibility for quality

Accountability is one of the most critical success factors to implement and sustain a quality culture. Leaders of medical product manufacturing companies must develop, implement, and foster a robust company culture focused on quality and compliance, not in cost. With the right quality culture and mindset, cost will go down because you will reduce scrap, rejection, rework, manufacturing deviations, laboratory failures, complaints, recall, regulatory issues, and so on.

Leaders must set the example. Site leaders must have full control of their site and not wait every month the visit from corporate leaders to discuss site's issues. CEOs and COOs cannot afford to have weak manufacturing site leadership either.

Nor a medical product manufacturing site can be managed remotely. Leaders and managers must go to the floor, must visit production areas, quality control laboratories, must know what is happening at their site.

The organization needs to make sure that all employees understand the quality performance expectations (see section 2.6) of their job and that all of them are held accountable for them. Accountability means that there are checks and balances being measured to make sure certain desired outcomes are being achieved. In our highly regulated industry, this is undoubtedly true. Samples from every batch of a medicine goes thru multiple inspections and tests before being released to the market. In the case of some medical devices, every *unit* goes thru inspections and analysis.

Although inspections and tests do not create quality, there are strict regulatory requirements to do that for medical products due to their criticality. For this reason, our industry is filled with highly redundant checks in form of inspections and audits to both, the product itself and the manufacturing records to verify that the activities were properly documented. Therefore, incorrect performance can be detected, and responsible personnel can be held accountable and receive feedback and coaching, very often in the form of ineffective retraining sessions that are repeated over and over again.

But when an adequate quality culture is implemented, it goes beyond accountability. Employees will do the right things not because they are being held accountable to them, but because the employees believe in and are committed to quality.

Competent, empowered and engaged people at all levels throughout the organization are essential to enhance its capability to create and deliver value. To manage an organization effectively and efficiently, it is necessary to involve all people at all levels and to respect them as individuals. Recognition, empowerment, and enhancement of competence facilitate the engagement of people in achieving the organization's quality objectives.

Management must be able to enroll everyone at every level of the organization to create and sustain the needed quality and compliance culture. The most effective culture is a culture of accountability and responsibility. In most organizations, accountability is something that happens to their people when things have gone wrong. To them, accountability is more about punishment than empowerment. In a culture of true accountability, people step forward and work hard to solve problems and get results. They do it willingly, not because some higher authority has ordered them to do it and not because they fear that not doing it will get them in trouble.

Creating a robust quality and compliance culture is not an option, it is a business necessity.

2.4 Sharing of knowledge and information

The sharing of information and knowledge keep a group together. What we communicate is a good reflection of our culture. You can tell a lot about the quality culture of an organization by their communication or lack of communication on the topic. If an organization is communicating about quality and compliance and sharing information regularly with their employees about the topic, then quality is probably an important part of their culture. If you are an outsider walking into an organization for the first time, there are visible demonstrations through communication that quality is important.

In contrast, even if the organization claims quality and compliance are important, but you do not see any visible demonstration of communication around the topic in meetings, company newsletter, websites, signs, and so on, then quality is probably not really an important element of their culture. Organizations and leaders tend to talk about and communicate what is truly important to them.

Communication is so important because words can encourage and educate. And they can influence behavior too. In other words, communication (sharing of knowledge and information) is a key component of a behavior-based quality system and quality culture.

Organizations with strong quality cultures know this and take the sharing of information beyond trainings. They share information often and communicate regularly with their employees about quality and compliance. Organizations with strong quality culture share information not just to convey knowledge and information, but to encourage their employees to action.

By using a variety of channels for sharing knowledge and information, an organization strengths quality and compliance as part of its culture. Posters, slogans, company's newsletter, are some common ways to communicate about quality and compliance. But are they effective in influencing behavior? Behavioral research indicates that generic messages with not specific instruction concerning the desired behavior or no mention of consequences have little impact on the target behavior.

One of the biggest errors in communication is the incorrect thinking that information equals communication. Talking to employees about quality and compliance is very different than having quality and compliance conversations with them. Conversations can help break down barriers and improve understanding.

A few good reasons why quality and compliance conversations are important? First, conversations about quality and compliance are important because they increase the likelihood that the message will be understood. Second, those conversations are important because they are participatory and not one-sided. By having a conversation about quality with employees, leaders can hear from them on issues of concern, their questions, and thoughts about quality and compliance. Finally, those conversations are important because they can help break down barriers and increase interpersonal connectedness – a critical part of shaping culture. Leaders and managers within the organization should ask questions related to quality and compliance in department and all-employees meetings or when walking around, for example during gemba walks.

How can you expect buy-in and support for employees in a remediation plan prepared in response to a tough regulatory inspection if the site management do not share any information beyond the plant's staff?

Sometimes it also happens at the consultant level. A company hires you to help with some specific problem, but you never receive the whole information.

2.5 Robust decision making and scientific, system-based approach to quality and compliance

Consistent and predictable results are achieved more effectively and efficiently when activities are understood and managed as interrelated processes that function as a coherent system.

Why so many pharmaceutical and medical devices companies have quality and compliance problems? It happens in despite of having hundreds of defined processes (a lot of standard operating procedures - SOPs), because having well defined processes and standards, training programs, inspection and testing and so on is not enough. Although we commonly refer to it as quality management *system*, all those elements are not well engrained in many companies. And therefore, they are not properly linked together or interrelated. And probably, the biggest problem is that the vast majority of QMS are not considering how these efforts might influence people's behaviors.

Definitively we must have well defined processes and standards as the base of our QMS. But having well defined processes and standards is not enough. We are missing the human factor: how the behavior of people using those well-defined processes and standards affect the final outcome?

Why do people not follow procedures?

Why people falsify data?

In section 1.9 we introduced the concept of House of Quality and established that one of the three basic pillars to sustain the QMS is the "people". You may have the best pharmaceutical quality system procedures and standards of the world but if they are not consistently put into practice by your employees, they are useless.

To have significant and sustainable improvement to your QMS you will need to improve the quality and compliance culture of your organization. At the end of the day, to improve the quality performance of your organization you must modify people's behaviors.

In our industry, the QMS of a medium-size pharmaceutical manufacturing site can include hundreds of procedures, work instructions, policies, standards and so on. In many cases, the number passes one thousand. These numbers alone can provide some idea of how complex is a QMS, and how intricate are the interrelationships between those processes. A critical characteristic of a system is that it cannot be fully explained by simply analyzing each of its components in isolation. It must be explained by understanding how each element interacts and influences other elements of the whole system. It is beyond a simplistic cause-and-effect relationship.

You can have the best documented quality system processes but it they are not consistently put in practice, they are useless. Consequently, our system must address both the science of quality and compliance and the dimensions of organizational culture and human behavior. And never forget that quality and compliance culture is part of a larger system, the overall culture of the organization. It is almost impossible to have a positive and strong quality culture if your organizational culture is not.

In our highly regulated environment, decision making must be risk-based and scientifically sounded. Implementation of risk management strategies is a fundamental element of the CGMP and QMS.

Risk management is an integral part of the medical product manufacturing QMS. Frequently, we observe specific actions and strategies studied and tackled in isolation, as individual components, not as a whole or complete system. Although this sort of linear cause-and-effect thinking in many instances has served us well (for example fixing a specific problem), it is not fully adequate to address many of the challenges we face, including those related to quality culture or employee's adherence to CGMP and expected behavior. This is because these issues involve multiple components that are interrelated.

Only by acquiring a systems-thinking mindset, can we adequately develop a behavior-based quality and compliance culture.

2.6 Creating quality and compliance performance expectations

When it comes to desired performance by employees, typically the common thinking is that the first step to achieve conformance is to provide adequate training to all concerned employees. This applies to all aspects of our QMS as training is considered one of the basic pillars of such management system, and personnel should be qualified to do the operations that are assigned to them in accordance with the nature of, and potential risk of, their operational activities.

Second in line should be the adequate supervision. When operating in a robust quality system environment, it is important that managers verify that skills gained from training are implemented in day-to-day performance. And in our very regulated industry, we perform a lot of analysis and testing to monitor the quality and safety of our medical products.

However, training, supervision and quality control are not the first steps in the process, and they are certainly not enough. Achieving excellence in quality starts before than this. This begins with creating quality and compliance performance expectations that are clear, achievable, and understood by all. Employees at all levels of the organization must know what is expected of them and what exactly they must do to achieve it. This is the first step in creating a behavior-based quality and compliance culture.

At the corporate level, the initial step is to establish a quality policy and associated quality objectives:

Quality Policy – A statement of intentions and direction issued by the highest level of the organization related to satisfying patients and user needs. It is like a strategic direction that communicates quality expectations that the organization is striving to achieve.

Quality Objectives – Specific measurable activities or processes to meet the intentions and directions as defined in the quality policy.

Getting employees to do what they are supposed to do

We already mentioned that quality and compliance must be everyone's job at any of our medical product companies. Patient safety is the first casualty when medical products have quality problems. Under a QMS, if everyone does whatever they are supposed to do (in other words, if their performance is the expected one), our medical products should have an optimal quality level. But the reality is very different. According to Fournier, the most common reason managers give as to why people at work do not do what they are supposed to do is, "they do not know what they are supposed to do." [22]

As a leader, you will get what you expect. If your expectations are unclear, employees will not know what you want them to do. If expectations are clear but low, you will obtain mediocre results. But if your expectations are clear, high, and uncompromising, you will get more.

Expect more than efficiency

Every medical product manufacturer in the world is focused in doing things more efficiently, in trying to reduce costs and expenses and be more competitive. But in addition to focus on doing things more efficiently, we should be equaled focused on doing things right. When it comes to medical product quality, almost right or pretty good may not be good enough. The same happens in the field of food safety. Think about a hamburger cooked to "almost" the right temperature. If it was contaminated with *Escherichia coli* 0157:H7, the result can be tragic[23].

Many medicines are manufactured in the form of coated pills. The coating is designed to hold the tablet together in the stomach and may

---

[22]Fournies, Ferdinad F. 1999. *Why employees don't do what they're supposed to do and what to do about it.* New York: McGraw Hill

[23]https://www.bmj.com/content/296/6626/875 accessed 2/03/2021

be there to protect the stomach from the medicine, protect the medicine from the acid in the stomach or to release the medicine after the stomach, for example, in the intestine. Lack of uniformity of coating is one frequent problem during the manufacture of those products and many times, batches are released to the marked with some units "almost coated". Is this an adequate expectation from patients? I do not think so. Every time a manufacturer approved a batch having this situation, what is the message conveyed to the employees?

When it comes to quality and compliance, establishing well-defined performance expectations is critical. Without them, you will not consistently get the right actions, outcomes, or results.

Attitude

When creating quality and compliance expectations, the best place to begin is to expect employees to have the proper quality and compliance mindset, aligned with the organization's principles and beliefs. You cannot force every employee in your organization to have the right quality and compliance attitude, but surely you can expect it and model it. Establishing an expectation that quality defects are preventable clearly communicate to each employee in the organization that they are expected to do their part in making quality product and maintaining compliance.

We live in an imperfect world but organizations and individuals that are always striving to get better are the ones that frequently do. In general, you will get more of what you tolerate. If your organization tolerates one good documentation practices deviation per batch, you will typically get more. If your organization tolerates that 5% or 10% of the affected employees can be untrained at the moment of implementing a new version of a procedure, then you will get more, and so on. On the other hands, if your organization operates under a zero-tolerance philosophy toward good documentation practices or training completion, then those quality issues will be less common, and the organization will be striving to get better.

We must expect every employee to have a right attitude about quality and compliance, because an employee with a right attitude will be much more likely to take right actions. Every day, each employee will influence those around him or her, whether we realize it or not. If they demonstrate a positive attitude toward quality and compliance, quality and compliance performance will increase exponentially because of their positive influence on other around them.

Be specific

Quality and compliance expectations must be clear and specific, not generic. Typically, slogans such as "quality first" or "quality is on your hands" may sound catchy, but they are not very effective. They do not tell an employee what it is that they must do to keep quality and compliance out of trouble. Those performance expectations must be related to specific task and behaviors. For example, if we established for production operators a "zero good documentation practices defect" for each manufacturing batch record, this expectation is clear, specific, and related to the documentation activities performed daily for those concerned operators. In general, most of your employees are genuinely interested in trying to do the right thing; but they need more than generic fancy slogans. Tell your employees in clear and user-friendly language *exactly* what they need to do to produce quality and compliant products.

Start with the CGMP and develop risk-based expectations

The main source of expectations for quality and compliance must be the current good manufacturing practices (CGMP) applicable to your products and markets. For example, CGMP for active ingredients can be found as part of the ICH Q7 guidance adopted worldwide as the CGMP model for active ingredient manufacture. For finished pharmaceutical and biopharmaceutical products, we have the U.S. FDA regulations laid out in 21 CFR 210 and 211 and numerous U.S. FDA guidance documents for industry. For marketed finished product in the European Union you must follow Eudralex Vol. 4 GMP guidelines, and so on.

All those CGMP documents depict a significant quantity of behavior-based quality and compliance performance expectations. They include issues ranging from employee health to personal hygiene to following procedures when performing activities and documenting activities at the time of performance. However, sometimes the language of the regulations must be further developed in our internal SOPs. For example, the U.S. FDA CGMP for finished pharmaceuticals establishes in its section 211.28 under Personal Responsibilities the "Personnel shall practice good sanitation and health habits". You better tell your employees exactly what that means. If you manufacture sterile products and you are having periodic contamination issues, this is a good area to begin your investigation. Data integrity is a significant issue for the medical product manufacturing industry. Worldwide regulatory authorities recently published guidance documents to describe clear expectations that can be easily transformed into a set of behavior-based quality and compliance expectations. In this specific case, there are some critical values involved such as integrity and honesty as part of the regulatory actions reported by authorities.

When creating quality and compliance performance expectations, they must be risk-based. In any organization, the analysis of the CAPA program should provide enough information regarding the most important behaviors that must be changed to increase the quality and compliance level. For example, in many companies, employees not following procedures is one of the most frequent and significant "root causes" for deviations and nonconformances (actually, it is not a root cause, it is just a symptom of deeper root causes). This is definitively a behavior that we must change. But first you should determine why they are not following procedures.

When you establish quality and compliance performance expectations you must think beyond mere regulatory compliance. Regulatory standards are generally considered a minimum standard. Think about all the things that your employees must know related to quality and compliance and clearly define what you want them to do.

Write them all down

Quality and compliance performance expectations must be documented, so that they are clear and communicated in a consistent manner and be easily understood by your employees. Quality and compliance expectations (as any other expectation) must be SMART:

- Specific – clear

- Measurable

- Achievable

- Relevant, risk-based

- <u>T</u>imely (realistic)

And finally, you will need to provide abundant education and training which is the next step in creating a behavior-based quality and compliance culture.

2.7 Educating and training to influence behavior; continually developing people's skills and knowledge

In any industry, when trying to achieve a certain set of desired performance behaviors (safety, quality, and so on), managers often turn to training as the solution.

In a survey related to food safety problems in the United States, authors found that deficient employee training was mentioned as number one[24]. In our industry, re-training is very often used as the main and/or only corrective action to fix deviations and nonconformities. This is so extended that in its first draft of the Quality Metrics' guidance, the U.S. FDA proposed to monitor the percentage of corrective actions that involved re-training of personnel as one of the two suggested key metrics for measure the quality culture of each manufacturing site. Moreover, the guidance mentioned that "FDA has observed that less robust quality systems often rely on preventing recurrence solely through personnel re-training (i.e., the same training has already been provided to the employee(s))".

Why we are re-training people over and over again?

Why employees that have been properly trained on how to do something yet fail to do it. Why is that?

[24]Sertkaya, A., Berlind, A, Lange, r. and Zink. D. 2006. Top ten food safety problems in the United States food processing industry. *Food Protection Trends, 26(5):* 310-315

The answer is simple and clear: it is because changing behaviors is not as simple as just providing training. What we know does not always equal what we do. Behavior change can be a difficult and complex process. Definitively it is more complex that simply provide (and documenting) training sessions.

In a QMS, personnel should be qualified to do the operations that are assigned to them in accordance with the nature of, and potential risk of, their operational activities. Under a quality system, managers should define appropriate qualifications for each position to help ensure that individuals are assigned appropriate responsibilities. Personnel should also understand the effect of their activities on the quality of product and the customer.

Under a quality system, continued training is critical to ensure that employees remain proficient in their operational functions and in their understanding of CGMP regulations. Typical quality systems training should address the policies, processes, procedures, and written instructions related to operational activities, the product/service, the quality system, and the desired work culture (for example, team building, communication, change, behaviors). Under a quality system, training should focus on both the employees' specific job functions and the related CGMP regulatory requirements. Managers are also expected to establish training programs that include the following:

- Evaluation of training needs

- Provision of training to satisfy these needs

- Evaluation of effectiveness of training

- Documentation of training and/or re-training

Under a quality system, senior management should support a problem-solving and communicative organizational culture. Managers should encourage communication by creating an environment that values employee suggestions and acts on suggestions for improvement. Management should also develop cross-functional groups to share ideas to improve procedures and processes.

Quality personnel must have a broad set of skills and knowledge than anyone in the organization as they are the ultimate responsible for the proper execution of the CGMP/QMS activities.

Although quality personnel should not take on the responsibilities of other units of the organization, these personnel should be selected based on their scientific and technical understanding, product knowledge, process knowledge and/or risk assessment abilities to appropriately execute quality functions (this quality systems feature is also found in the CGMP regulations, which identify specific qualifications, such as education, training, and experience or any combination thereof (see § 211.25(a) and (b)).

When operating in a robust quality system environment, it is essential that managers verify that skills gained from training are implemented in day-to-day performance. This concept of verification of training effectiveness and an overall discussion of training topics can be found in Chapter 6.

We must educate and train our employees to increase their competences and to influence their behaviors.

2.8 Developing quality and compliance goals and metrics

Every company must define adequate key quality performance indicators (KQPI) or quality metrics, as well as the data collection process to be reported and their respective responsible. KQPI are lead metrics that will support company in developing and sustaining a strong, positive quality and compliance culture. There are inherent links between culture, behavior, and leading quality indicators that drive desired patient-focused behaviors. Monitoring and surveillance of key triggers and the design of leading quality indicators are highly recommended practices to help shape cultural excellence.

Setting goals and measuring performance against those goals are critical components to develop a behavior-based quality culture, but they must be done and used correctly to be effective. Goals are effective because, when they are established appropriately, they are powerful antecedents to desired performance or behavior. An antecedent is anything that comes before a behavior that contains information about behavioral consequences. Accordingly, goals alone will not result in improved performance unless they are consistently paired with consequences. section 2.9 discussed this topic in detail.

Typically, most -if not all- quality metrics used by our industry are outcome-based measures (*lagging* indicators). Although such indicators are important and useful to detect trend and establish priorities, we must be clear that to establish and sustain a strong, positive quality culture, we need to change behaviors (*leading* indicators).

On the other hand, leading metrics and indicators are inputs that help to predict the future. They define what actions are necessary to achieve goals with measurable outcomes. They "lead" to successfully meeting overall business objectives such as create and maintain a strong, positive quality and compliance culture. In the following pages we discuss the FDA's Quality Metrics Program including the originally three voluntary ones related to quality culture. Table 2.2 below depicts typical examples of lagging and leading indicators in the pharmaceutical industry. Chapter 4 discusses a robust set of lead quality indicators.

Table 2.2 Examples of lagging and leading quality indicators

Lagging Indicators	Leading Indicators
• Quantity of critical/major deviations per batch • Out of Specification (OOS) rate (of total tests performed for each category) • Lot acceptance rate • Overall lead-time per batch (days) • Customer complaint rate • Past-due CAPA actions	• Turnover rate • Preventive action / corrective action rate • Cross-training plans rate • Calibration on time rate • Personnel developmental plans rate • Preventive maintenance on time rate • Participation in the quality improvement ideas program

It is important to remember that CGMP inspections as well as internal audits have been historically used to catch people doing things wrong or detect conditions that do not meet a particular standard or requirement. When developing a behavior-based management system, you must think differently. You need to think about all that you do, including measurements, in terms of human behavior and motivation. In other words, (*leading*) measurements should be conducted to catch people doing things right, not catch them doing things wrong.

Lead key quality performance metrics and indicators should measure factors related to human behavior and organizational culture that are critical for quality to success such as processes, knowledge, and behaviors.

Measure processes - measuring end states for the processes (for example final release attributes) is not good enough. You should measure and evaluate critical quality attributes for your products at appropriate steps (incoming, in process, final release, stability) as applicable. Pass or fail is not good enough; you need to know if the results are consistently achieved. For example, you must implement adequate measures of process capability using adequate indicators.

Process Capability/Performance was one of the FDA's originally proposed optional three metrics to be used as evidence of manufacturing robustness and as commitment to quality. FDA recognized the importance of statistical process control as a tool in understanding and managing variability in both product and processing for drug products in measuring and evaluating process stability and process capability. FDA requires manufacturers to apply statistical tools in a manner appropriate to assure that the product and process reproducibly meet specifications on an ongoing basis. Specifications must be meaningful in terms of achieving the desired finished product characteristics. This data enables science and risk-based quality risk management by identifying when manufacturing improvement is needed.

Measure knowledge –training, competence, and performance are not synonyms as discussed in section 6.1. Most pharmaceutical companies do not formally determine the effectiveness of the training processes (refer to Chapter 6 in general and section 6.6 in particular). Patients need competent operators making their medicines, not just trained operators.

Measure behavior – it has been said, what we know is of little consequence, it is what we do that is important. Do employees actually do what they are expected and trained to do? To know that we must measure specific behaviors or activities. Although measuring behaviors or activities can be difficult and time consuming, it is a necessary activity in order determine if they are being done consistently and correctly. Think for example in aseptic technique training which is a critically paramount knowledge for sterile manufacturing. You can provide training. Measure knowledge (through writing exams, case studies, and so on) but you must, periodically, witness activities to determine if the knowledge translate into correct behaviors. There are a lot of FDA inspectional observations for sterile sites derived from visual observation of operators' behavior through a window or from video recording evaluation. Inadequate pipetting or other laboratory techniques is another area where the direct observation of behavior has not substitute.

A list of positive behaviors associated to a strong, positive quality culture is included in Chapter 3.

FDA's quality metrics related to quality culture

In the previously cited 2015 draft guidance for industry, the FDA proposed three optional, voluntary metrics to try to get at the elusive quality culture. The first metric proposed was intended to measure senior management engagement by assessing whether the head of the quality unit and the head of the operations unit have signed the annual product review (APR) or product quality review (PQR). The second optional metric proposed was related to corrective action and preventive action (CAPA) effectiveness. The measurement for this metric is to indicate the percentage of corrective actions that required retraining of personnel, the assumption being that the root cause of the original deviation (real or due to insufficient analysis) was determined to be insufficient or ineffective training. The third proposed metric was intended to measure a firm's process capabilities.

Chapter 4 discusses an ample list of key leading quality culture indicators.

2.9 Using consequences to increase or decrease behaviors

Consequences are important because they increase of decrease the likelihood of behavior occurring again. Behavioral consequences are those things and events that follow a behavior and change the probability that the behavior will be repeated in the future. Consequences must be used to shape and reinforce adequate positive behaviors towards quality and compliance.

The word consequence is often interpreted to have a negative connotation, but consequences can be negative, and they can be also positive. Remember that quality performance is the result of people's behavior. If a company is not seeing improvements in quality, then one contributing factor may be that they are not effectively using consequences to manage performance.

From the point of view of behavioral sciences, *positive reinforcement* and *negative reinforcement* are two behavioral consequences that increase the probability of a behavior occurring again. On the other hand, *punishment* and *penalty* are two behavioral consequences that decrease behavior.

We can simplify the discussion by calling them either positive or negative consequences. Positive consequences are consequences that increase the likelihood of the behavior occurring again. Negative consequences generally decrease the likelihood of the behavior or, alternative, are viewed as useful in trying to sustain certain desired behaviors out of fear of receiving a negative consequence.

For example, a person driving might choose to follow the speed limit (desired behavior) and not speed (undesired behavior) out of concern of receiving a speeding ticket (negative consequence). Management created consequences do not occur naturally. They only happen when a manager causes them to. They require consistent management observation, commitment, and follow through. For example, if when employees demonstrate a certain behavior, the manager gives them a small reward and thanks them, this is an intentionally created positive consequence.

Our industry has been focused historically in creating negative consequences for substandard quality performance. From internal audits to management reviews, violations on CGMP are escalated to senior management. Regulatory authorities may threaten establishments with warning letters and other regulatory enforcement actions. Fears of punishment and penalties have been one of the primary tools used by regulatory agencies in attempt to enhance compliance. However, if we place an overreliance on negative consequences, it demonstrates that we really do not understand how to utilize consequences to drive enhanced performance.

A work environment driven by fear of negative consequences is not a very nice work environment. Although negative consequences certainly have their place in managing quality and compliance performance, they are not the only consequences that should be used.

An adequate balance between positive and negative consequences, sometimes referred to as positive and negative reinforcement, with emphasis on positive ones, generally leads to enhanced performance and results. Companies should consider two basic questions:

- What should the company positively reinforce?

- What are the types of positive consequences or reinforcement the company should consider?

Specific desired behaviors, as described in Chapter 3, should be the target of frequent recognition in order to reinforce them. This type of recognition is viewed as in-the-spot, individualized, and informal reinforcement. It includes a simple verbal "thank you". Most employees sincerely appreciate verbal recognition by their managers or leaders. Other types of positive reinforcement can range from more formal token of appreciation, such as quality cards, to small gift certificates worth monetary value. You want to reach the right balance between creating positive consequences and recognition for a job well done or doing the extra mile versus simply recognizing employees for what they are expected to do.

Sites and departments that are showing significant improvements, meeting established targets or goals, or whose performance is considered best in class for the company, should be recognized. As summarized by Michael LeBoeuf in his book *The greatest Management Principle in the World* (1985), managers do not get what they hope for, train for, beg for, or even demand. Managers get what they recognize and reward through positive consequences.

We have reviewed how management-created positive consequences can be used to increase the likelihood of desired behaviors re-occurring. However, sometimes the behavior that is occurring is an undesired one and we want it to stop. In these situations, negative consequences can be used to decrease the likelihood of an undesired behavior from occurring again.

Although negative consequences may be effective in influencing short-term behavioral change, there is doubts about their ability to produce real, long-term behavioral change. When management has a pep talk to employees about recent mishaps and warning them that the next employee having such a mishap will be terminated, certainly it will be an immediate, but temporal, change. But if the real root causes of those mishaps are not corrected, they will occur again. On the other hand, the intentional violation of procedures (think about data integrity problems) must be integrated into the disciplinary management process already established at the company.

In summary, remember that behavioral change is complex and that consequences are only one small component of a comprehensive behavior-based quality and compliance culture.

2.10 Commitment to resilience: learn from errors

Resilience is a combination of keeping errors small, of improvising workarounds that keep the system functioning, and of absorbing change while persisting. It is concerned with the ability of organizations to not only effectively anticipate errors but also to cope with and bounce back from errors and unexpected events.

One of the most common descriptions of the High Reliability Organization (HRO) is that it is "resilient." Here is how the Oxford English Dictionary defines resilient:

1. The capacity to recover quickly from difficulties, toughness.

2. The ability of a substance to spring back into shape; elasticity.

The definition points directly at two important characteristics of organizational resilience. First, organizations show resilience in response to a difficulty or deformity. Resilience is reactive, not predictive. Thus, it is not the kind of capacity that is based on a careful analysis of potential faults, with mitigating solutions pre-positioned to cope. In fact, the resilient organization will generate solutions to unexpected problems on the fly.

The second feature is that when an unexpected problem occurs, the elastic (resilient) organization will continue to function normally. It continues to produce desired outcomes despite the problem (and internalizes the solution so that a future response to the problem is even faster).

Weick and Sutcliffe (2007) summarize the resilient organization very clearly:

In moments of resilience, conditions vary yet the effect remains the same. That difference lies at the heart of a commitment to resilience.

The "commitment to resilience" implies that the company's leadership and culture have the proper attitude toward unexpected conditions or failures. It emphasizes the central point that high reliability organizations are not organizations that do not experience failure. Rather, they continue to generate the main outcomes of their mission despite failures. To adapt to something unexpected, the people in the company are ready to recognize the event for what it is, avoid complacent assumptions, and refuse to oversimplify or routinize the problem before an effective solution is identified. This is a capacity that organizations with a commitment to resilience will develop over time.

Employees in resilient organizations will create innovative responses to failures as needed, almost improvising in real time. However, they are not working in an unstructured system when they do this. They need to have both expertise regarding the portion of the organization affected by an event and need the confidence to act as developed by prior empowering support from leaders and managers.

Probably in our industry, the best area to demonstrate resilience is the handling of human errors and mistakes in our operations, with the ultimate objective of reducing them as lower as human possible. To be able to do this, first we need:

1. Clearly understand the *human error* concept

2. Identify *human factors* affecting the performance of your processes

3. Establish *effective* barriers and corrective and preventive actions related to those human factors

When an operator does not properly execute a manufacturing step, we immediately label it as human error. When we investigate the situation, inadequate training and supervision, lack of clarity in the work instruction, and multitasking can be factors behind the operator's mistake. Human errors and mistakes are the symptoms of *causal (human) factors* associated with root causes that we must discover prior to solving them.

Chapters 5, 6, and 7 respectively cover the main human factors associated to personnel, training, and QMS documentation. Our book in the topic of Human Error reduction in Manufacturing presents a detailed discussion of human errors and human factors[25].

[25]Rodríguez-Pérez, José. 2018. *Human Error Reduction in Manufacturing.* Milwaukee: ASQ Quality Press

Chapter 3
Quality Behaviors

This Chapter details a comprehensive set of desired behaviors associated to a positive, strong quality and compliance culture that support the ten principles described in the previous Chapter. These behavioral criteria are described in their desired states and they are presented under the principle most directly affected by each one. However, most of these behaviors affect to a wide range of principles. Quality behaviors are:

Behaviors observed at the site or organization that are associated with a strong quality culture in areas such as leadership, clear communication and transparency, commitment and engagement, technical excellence, and standardization of requirements.

Principle 1 – Leadership at the top
Leaders and senior managers should:

- Establish company values that include quality

- Establish a culture of trust and integrity

- Encourage a company-wide commitment to quality

- Be positive examples of quality mindset to people in the company

- Be accountable for actions and decisions, particularly delegated activities

- Allocate resources to meet quality and regulatory expectations

- Sponsor the establishment of a quality improvement ideas program at every site

- Be quality ambassadors inside and outside the company

Principle 2 – Clear management visibility and leadership

Managers should:

- Facilitate escalation of issues

- Promote continuous improvement

- Promote collaboration throughout the company

- Be positive examples of quality mindset to people in the company

- Questioning or challenging non-added value activities

- Take personal/individual accountability (own the issue) to solve problems

- Participate in Gemba walks to create visible management commitment and to engage employees at all levels of the company

- Do the right thing when no one is watching

- Tell the boss what they need to know and not just what they want to hear

- Display updated quality metrics (right first-time figures, excellence targets on defects, rejects, and so on, near each production/work area)

- Communicate (broadly) the vision, mission and strategy of the company

- Communicate regularly on quality topics and the importance of quality.

- Consider (always) both, quality and business aspects when have quality issues in conflict with business issues, before deciding

- Provide sufficient and adequate support and coaching to line workers to help them improve quality

- Model (always) the desired behavior of "doing the right thing" on issues of quality

- Practice (routinely) on a day-to-day basis, the desired quality behaviors, for example, through Gemba walks

- Identify (routinely) and implement (as appropriate) opportunities for continuous improvement

- Conduct survey to assess people's satisfaction, communicate the results and take appropriate actions

- Communicate (broadly) the vision, mission and strategy of the company communicated and lived by our employees

- Enable employees at all levels within the company to identify and communicate risks

Principle 3 – Accountability at all levels
Everyone, as applicable, should:

- Put patients ahead of everything else

- See quality as a personal responsibility

- Review quality issues, including executive level and/or CEO level staff

- Provide people with the required resources, training, and authority to act with accountability

- Put "quality is everyone's responsibility" in practice

- Hold people accountable and take personal/individual accountability

- Establish training on proper business conduct including good data management with mechanisms like hotlines and/or emails to promote reporting of issues

- Choose leaders who exemplify quality culture behaviors

- Facilitate the escalation of quality issues

- Promote continuous improvement

- Question or challenge non-added value activities

- Do the right thing when no one is watching

- Tell what the boss needs to know not just what he/she wants to hear

- Encourage staff's understanding of their individual impact on quality

- Be able to routinely explain what quality information is tracked and why and outline their role in the achievement of quality goals

- Be involved in problem identification, problem solving, troubleshooting, and investigations throughout cross-functional teams including line workers

- Live the vision, mission, and strategies for quality

- Strive continuously to reduce any kind of waste in every process

- Participate in improvement projects, including managers

- Have sufficient authority to make decisions and feel trusted to do their jobs well

- Regularly identify issues and proactively intervene to minimize any potential negative impact on quality and compliance

- Not be afraid to speak up and identify quality issues, as they believe management will act on their suggestions

Principle 4 – Sharing of knowledge and information
Everyone, as applicable, should:

- Actively listen and engage in two-way communication

- Encourage honest dialog

- Share information on quality performance with other employees and partners

- Behave in a proactive and transparent manner with regulators

- Use Gemba walks as an enabler for communication of site priorities/ challenges and how the area's contributes to the success of the site

- Follow through on pending issues

- Communicate on a needed basis

- Manage communication to continuously reinforce quality expectations

- Present quality topics at every monthly department meeting

- Participation of head of departments in management review

- Present quality topic(s) at every all-employees meeting of the site

- Establish formal mechanism to effectively manage the supply chain, including both suppliers and customers

Principle 5 – Robust decision making and scientific, system-based approach to quality and compliance

Leaders and managers should:

- Establish proper Business Conduct programs with mechanisms to promote reporting of issues

- Manage risk that can affect outputs of the process and overall outcomes of the QMS and finally affect the safety and effectiveness of our products

- Implement continuous improvement programs that measure progress (Six Sigma, Kaizen, performance Boards, Cost of Quality, and so on)

- Establish and maintain a QMS that has clear performance criteria

- Follow clear and transparent governance processes

- Conduct internal survey on company's quality culture

- Establish site specific requirements (when necessary) and not standardized across the entire company

- Establish/follow a program of risk management and preventive quality

- Ensure product quality is not compromised during implementation of lean manufacturing or other process improvement efforts

- Proactive handling of the supply chain

- Use documented operating procedures to standardize our processes

- Measure continuously the quality of process by using process measures

- Ensure that the maintenance department focuses on assisting machine operators perform their own preventive maintenance

- Emphasize good maintenance as a key strategy for increasing quality

- Continuously optimize the site maintenance program based on a dedicated failure analysis

Principle 6 – Creating quality and compliance performance expectations
Leaders and managers should:

- Establish cross functional quality and compliance goals

- Ensure that quality metrics and goals are consistently designed and selected to promote/motivate desired quality behaviors

- Ensure that updated quality metrics (right first-time figures, excellence targets on defects, rejects, and so on) are regularly posted and easily visible near each production/work area

- Continuously measure the quality of processes by using process measures

Principle 7 – Educating and training to influence behavior; continually developing people's skills and knowledge

Leaders and managers should:

- Hire individuals with appropriate technical expertise for their role

- Be eager to share knowledge and expertise to solve problems

- Promote individuals based on performance and technical expertise

- Facilitate participation in external technical conferences and workshops

- Adopt a Quality by Design (QbD) mindset and approach

- Promote the application of new technologies (PAT, continuous manufacturing, and so on)

- Ensure that employees regularly receive training that effectively helps them ensure quality in their work fostering a learning company

- Educate and train people at all levels

- Develop subject matter experts

- Ensure people are competent to successfully perform their duties

- Promote the establishment of developmental plans for people at all levels of the company

- Recognize and acknowledge accomplishments

- Promote the measurement of training effectiveness

Principle 8 – Developing quality and compliance goals and metrics
Leaders and managers should:

- Establish quality goals and objectives linked and aligned with company strategy and goals

- Monitor leading quality and compliance metrics

- Act on negative trends

- Be regularly involved in reviewing and assessing product, process, and quality management system performance

Principle 9 – Using consequences to increase or decrease behaviors
Leaders and managers should:

- Encourage and reward "speaking up" regarding quality issues

- Provide timely feedback and coaching of job performance to employees

- Offer non-monetary recognition to individuals who achieve or support quality goals

- Offer financial incentives linked to achieving quality goals

- Routinely recognize and celebrate both individual and group improvement achievements in performance quality

- Recognize and acknowledge people's contributions, learning and improvement

- Inspire, encourage, and recognize people's contribution

Principle 10 – Commitment to resilience: learn from errors
Leaders and managers should:

- Ensure that there is no tendency to point fingers and to lay blame to others

- Quickly acknowledge improvement opportunities and problems

- Formally review mistakes and errors and look to share and learn from them

- Implement a human factor program aimed to understand and minimize the causes of human errors

Chapter 4
Quality Culture Indicators

L ead key quality performance metrics and indicators should measure factors related to human behavior and organizational culture that are critical for quality to success such as processes, knowledge, and behaviors.

It is necessary to establish a periodic *Quality Culture Management Review*. Between three or four meetings per calendar year can be an appropriate frequency for these quality culture or cultural excellence reviews. The analysis of those indicators should be performed using trends.

If you do not have historical data to establish the baseline for each of the indicators (which will be the case, for example, for new ones), it is recommended to implement the metric (for example, deployment of the *Quality Improvement Ideas* program) and establish your initial baseline using data from the first quarter of semester since its implementation. Thereafter, the company should aim a realistic improvement for the next period. For example, a 15% increase in participation in the next semester.

This Chapter discusses an ample list of those indicators divided into the following three general categories:

a) Leadership engagement

b) People engagement

c) Culture and maturity

For each of the indicators, a description is provided along with the recommended goal(s). Unless otherwise indicated under the specific indicator, the measurement should be performed using specific report generated by responsible area/department.

Each metric measures the performance of the specific indicator during the period under review, for example, the last quarter or the last semester.

Leadership Engagement

1. Quality and compliance goals established for all employees.
   Goal is 100%

2. Quality and compliance topics always included in periodic department meetings (monthly frequency recommended).
   Goal is 100%

3. Periodic (at least once every two months) *communications* to all employees about quality initiatives/quality topics, including all-employees *meetings* (at least once every semester).
   Goal is 100%

4. Managers participation in internal audits (% of audits having at least one manager as part of the audit team).
   Goal is 100%

5. Managers participation in supplier audits (% of audits having at least one manager as part of the audit team).
   Goal is 100%

   Note: even if supplier audits are performed by corporate auditor, it is encouraged to include managers from the specific manufacturing site as part of the audit team.

6. Managers participation in improvement projects (% of improvement projects having at least one manager as part of the team).
   Goal is 100%

7. Head of departments participation in Quality Management Review Meetings.
   Goals is 100%

8. Head of departments participation in Quality Culture Management Review Meetings.
   Goals is 100%

9. Head of departments participation in GEMBA/facilities walkthroughs.
   Goal is to have at least 50% of site's head of departments participating in every GEMBA walk.

10. Quantity of improvement projects generated from GEMBA/ facility walkthroughs.
    Goal is 20% increasing in number of projects for the next quarter versus baseline of previous quarter. The % of increase should be lowered as the quantity of projects become bigger.

11. Participation of leadership in external forums/conferences.
    Goal is to have every leader/senior manager participating in at least one external forum/conference every year.

People Engagement

12. Every site implements/maintains a Quality Improvement Ideas program with two key indicators:
    a. Quantity of ideas submitted per 100 employees
    b. Quantity of ideas submitted per employee per department
    Goal is having a 20% increasing in quantity of ideas in both indicators versus the baseline of previous quarter.

13. Cross-training plans.
    Goal is to have at least 5% of managerial employees participating in cross-training plans at any time.

14. Developmental plans.

Goal is to develop and implement developmental plan for 100% of managerial employees.

15. Technical training hours per employee: CGMP, quality, compliance, and related technical topics.
Goal is 5% increasing quarterly versus the baseline of the previous period.

16. Site employees' attendance to external courses/conferences (in person or virtual).
Goal is 5% increasing quarterly versus the baseline of the previous period.

17. External certifications (for example, ASQ, Lead auditor, and so on) per 100 employees.
Goal is 5% increasing quarterly versus the baseline of the previous quarter.

18. Turnover monthly rate.
Goal is 0%

19. Periodic (annually) survey of employees' satisfaction.
Goal is to perform at least one survey annually.

20. Periodic (annually) survey of quality culture.
Goal is to perform at least one survey annually.

21. Employee recognition section included in periodic department meetings.
Goal is 100% of the meeting have this recognition section.

22. Employee recognition section included in periodic all-employees meetings.
Goal is 100% of all-employees meetings have this recognition section.

Culture and Maturity

23. Level of qualifications (academic degrees, bachelor, master, doctorate) per 100 employees.
    For the goal, we recommend establish the baseline based on the current situation (for example, 12% of current employees of the site have at least a bachelor's degree), and then establish a goal of *realistic* improvement during the next period.

24. QA indirect labor rate: number of QA full-time employees/total full-time employee of the site.
    For the goal, we recommend establish the baseline based on the current situation and then establish a goal of *realistic* improvement during the next period.

25. Training coverage: 100% of affected personnel trained *before* implementation of a revised QMS document.
    Goal is 100% of updated QMS documents implemented *after* 100% of affected personnel were trained.

26. Training effectiveness monitoring rate.
    Goal is 100% of training include a mechanism for verification of training's effectiveness.

27. Re-training CAPAs rate: What percentage of corrective actions involved re-training of personnel.
    Goal is 0%
    Note: As the ideal goal is probably not realistic, we suggest establishing a baseline during one quarter and then establish a realistic % reduction target for next period.

28. Training needs assessment (TNA) review for each position/function.
    Goal is 100% of TNA having less than 1 year since last review.

29. Human error investigations rate.
    Goal is 0%

Note: As the ideal goal is probably not realistic, we suggest establishing a baseline during one quarter and then establish a realistic % reduction target for next period.

30. Establish and maintain a Human Factor program at the site.

31. Job description annual periodic review.
Goal is 100% of job description having less than 1 year since last review.

32. Establish and maintain Process Capability of performance index for each critical quality attribute (CQA).
Goal is 100% of CQA have updated process capability index.

33. Continued Process Verification (CPV) monitored, as applicable, for:
a. Finished products CQAs
b. Significant incoming and in-process quality attributes
c. APIs final CQAs
Goal is 100% of required CPVs are maintained.

34. Equipment/area qualification on time rate.
Goal is 100% as per site schedule.

35. Validation (process, cleaning, computer system validation, and so on) on time rate.
Goal is 100% for each type of validation as per site schedule.

36. CAPA plans effectiveness measurement rate.
Goal is 100% of CAPA plans have a formal, documented effectiveness measured.

37. CAPA plans effectiveness rate.
Goal is 100% of actions declared as effective.

38. Preventive versus corrective actions rate.
Goal is to have a ratio >/= to 1.

39. Risk management plan for all key processes developed, implemented, and updated, at least, annually.
Goal is 100%

40. APR/PQR on time review (per SOP requirement) rate.
Goal is 100%

41. APR/PQR review level rate: review by site leader and site quality head.
Goal is 100%

42. Establish and maintain an effective risk-based Internal Audit Program.
Goal is 100% of internal audits performed as per approved schedule.

43. Establish and maintain a risk-based Supplier Certification program.
Goal is 100% of supplier audits performed as per approved schedule.

44. Calibration on time rate.
Goal is 100% as per site schedule.

45. Preventive maintenance (PM) on time rate.
Goal is 100% as per site schedule.

46. Quality metrics boards updated frequently.
Goal is100% of the boards updated at least every week.

47. Implementation of reinforcement programs such as coaching, mentorship, and so on.
For the goal, we recommend establish the baseline based on the current situation (percentage of employees currently involved in these programs) and then establish a goal of *realistic* improvement during the next period.

Chapter 5
The Pillars: People

People are the most important element of any enterprise. At the same time, it is the most vulnerable and weak link of the system. Quality is pursued in many ways, from informal approaches to a systematic, enterprise level operating under certification to ISO 9001:2015 or other standards. A common challenge is the difficulty in encouraging people to engage with those arrangements within the context of their cultures, traditional work values, perceptions, and practices.

5.1 People Engagement

In a more general context, people engagement is the emotional commitment that people have to the organization and its goals. This emotional commitment means engaged people actually care about their work and their organization. They do not work for just a paycheck, or just for the next promotion, but work towards the organization's goals. When we consider engagement with quality, it is an extension of this emotional commitment.

A strong, positive quality culture, where people agree upon and care deeply about organizational values, can improve organization performance, motivate people and coordinate their behaviors towards a vision and specific performance goals.

Engagement with the quality of products and services and the QMS has many facets. Without genuine alignment, quality remains a disconnected component of the organization. Alignment transforms this situation and shows the high-level value that can be contributed.

Engagement with those at operational levels is also key. The actions at that level should serve to provide far more relevance to the activities of people and the requirements of the quality management system. Many challenges with people engagement arise from the lack of relevance. There are many examples of the QMS being "those files in the computer" and people being in charge of audits and correcting "people" when things go wrong.

As established in the International Standard *ISO 10018 Quality management – Guidance for people engagement,* an organization can benefit from contributions to the development of its vision and strategy from a wider range of people, not only top management. Clear benefits of people engagement to the organization's strategic direction and overall success include:

a) greater involvement and contributions of the organization's staff

b) greater clarity to personnel in understanding their individual roles in implementing the strategy

c) improved people's competence

d) achieving the organization's vision and strategy

e) improved performance

f) better engagement

g) higher levels of customers and employees satisfaction

h) improved productivity

5.2 Effective Supervision

Nowadays, many organizations are structured to have insufficient supervision of jobs. Supervision can and normally does play a key role in the selection of the right worker for the job, scheduling of workers to match the tasks required for the day/week, and generally overseeing task execution to ensure that policies and procedures are followed. Supervisors are not always trained on all of their key roles in support of control of human factors, such as detecting issues in workers related to fitness for duty or fatigue, to mention just a few.

Providing an effective level of supervision is critical for reliable operations in the manufacturing industries. Supervision can be considered a management function, a control in the organization to manage performance and quality of work. People in supervisory functions need appropriate technical and nontechnical competencies in order to perform effectively. However, they are often insufficiently prepared for this critical role, especially for the nontechnical aspects.

Supervision involves controlling, influencing, and leading a group of people to ensure that activities are performed correctly, in an effective and efficient manner.

In addition to the lack of nontechnical competencies (which influence how a supervisor performs the role), one of the biggest problems is where supervisors perform their function. In today's industrial environment, supervisors spend most of their time far from production lines or work sites. A day full of meetings, from planning production to discussing human resources issues, is the norm for most supervisors. Supervisors need to be on the floor, directly controlling, influencing, and leading the team. The English verb supervise originated from the medieval Latin *supervisus*, past participle of *supervidēre*, from Latin *super-* + *vidēre* (to see). Therefore, the original definition of the function includes the need for physical contact between supervisor and supervisees. When supervisors are far from work sites they cannot supervise effectively.

Earlier, we mentioned that technical and nontechnical competencies are necessary to become an effective supervisor or team leader. Typically, in the regulated industries, supervisors are developed and promoted from within, and they have the required technical knowledge and experience. However, very often they lack many of the nontechnical competencies (behaviors) necessary to become a successful supervisor. Some examples of these nontechnical competencies required by today's supervisors are depicted in Table 5.1.

Table 5.1 Examples of non-technical supervisory competences

Supervisory Competency	Example Behaviors
Ensure compliance	• Positive: Monitor performance and check compliance. Emphasize quality and safety over production quotes and schedule. Set the example and explain to the team that compliance is expected and required at all times. • Negative: Set a poor example by breaking rules or procedures, cutting corner, and so on.
Encourage the team	• Positive: Seek the team's ideas for quality improvements. Act on quality concerns or ideas to improve. Manage and developing the team. • Negative: Ignore the team's ideas for improvement or concern about quality or safety.
Involve the team	• Positive: Support and encourage quality activities. Help the team to learn from incidents. Initiate discussion about performance improvements. • Negative: Focus on punitive actions in response to human error; impose production quotas.

5.3 Adequate Staffing

An adequately staffed organization ensures that personnel are available with the proper qualifications for both planned and foreseeable unplanned activities. Staffing is a dynamic process in which plant management monitors personnel performance to ensure that overall organizational performance goals are met or exceeded. The result of an effective staffing process is a balance between personnel costs and the achievement of organizational goals. Issues with staffing may include:

- Selection of the right staff for a job

- Avoiding staff overload

- Rotating staff on tasks that require high concentration, such as quality inspections

Each organization requires the proper amount and type of expertise to competently operate under a variety of conditions. The term *expertise* includes the attributes of talent, effectiveness, knowledge, skills, abilities, and experience necessary to operate and maintain plant systems, structures, and components.

Staffing is concerned with having the optimal number and type of personnel to consistently perform at the required standard, and obviously it is intrinsically tied to workload. *Workload* relates to the total demand placed on a person as he or she performs a task. It refers to both the quantity of work and the quality or complexity of the work. There is a clear understanding that both excessive and very low workloads lead to human errors. In the first case, the worker is overwhelmed by the activity. In the second case, workers will mentally disengage from the process and be less effective.

Questions about workload are one of the most common and controversial issues in human factors because of its relationship to staffing levels. When asked, workers will claim that they are overworked, while management will claim that there is too much unproductive idle time. The right staffing level provides adequate resources to do the necessary tasks, and those tasks should be distributed in a way that keeps each worker near an optimum stress level. The ideal workload should be challenging enough to maintain the worker's attention and interest without overloading them.

Adequate staffing and workload are critical factors in achieving safe and effective performance. These factors can be easily overlooked during times of staff reduction, resulting in situations where the remaining staff try to work harder, quicker, or longer (and probably take shortcuts) to compensate. In addition to delaying some tasks (or simply not doing them), error rates will increase. Sometimes, regulated companies see a spike in human error after the implementation of lean programs because a typical outcome of these programs is staff reduction.

Regulators consider staffing a critical issue in producing safe and effective medical products. For example, the U.S. FDA finished pharmaceutical CGMP requires under §211.25 _Personnel qualifications_ that "(c) There shall be an **adequate number** of qualified personnel to perform and supervise the manufacture, processing, packing, or holding of each drug product."

The European pharmaceutical GMP regulations require under the _Principle of Chapter 2: Personnel_ that "The correct manufacture of medicinal products relies upon people. For this reason, there must be **sufficient qualified personnel** to carry out all the tasks which are the responsibility of the manufacturer."[26]

It is important to recognize that workload does not maintain a simple linear relationship with performance. Both sustained low workload and high workload may adversely affect performance, as explained by the Yerkes-Dodson law, which establishes that there is an empirical relationship between arousal and performance.[27] The law was originally developed by psychologists Robert M. Yerkes and John Dillingham Dodson in 1908 and dictates that performance increases with physiological or mental arousal (pressure), but only up to a point. When levels of arousal become too high, performance decreases. The process is often illustrated graphically as a bell-shaped curve that increases and then decreases with higher levels of arousal.

Without enough pressure, a worker can become bored, unmotivated, frustrated, and lose situational awareness and alertness, among other undesirable effects. On the other hand, under too much pressure, the worker will become anxious, fatigued, or emotionally drained. Both situations are considered as stress states, which make error more likely. Workload modeling is a complex activity typically undertaken by human factors experts in fields such as air traffic control.

Many of the human errors and other frequent problems within the regulated industries can be, in some way or another, related to workload

[26]https://ec.europa.eu/health/sites/health/files/files/eudralex/vol-4/2014-03_chapter_2.pdf, accessed 2/04/2021
[27]https://hbr.org/2016/04/are-you-too-stressed-to-be-productive-or-not-stressed-enough, accessed 2/04/2021

and staffing issues. Possible solutions to these problems include improvements to the following areas:

- Work area

- Allocation of functions

- Work environment

- Work equipment

- Task design

- Resource allocation

- Recruitment and selection

- Skill, knowledge, and experience

One of the most important aspects influencing the physical and mental condition of a person is the degree to which employees are able to recover from the fatigue and stress of work. Work breaks can potentially be disruptive to the flow of work and impact the completion of a task. However, breaks can serve multiple positive functions for the person being interrupted,[28] such as:

- Stimulation for the individual performing a job that is routine or boring

- Opportunities to engage in activities that are essential to emotional well-being

- Sustained job satisfaction

[28]Jett, Quintus R., Jennifer M. George. 2003. Work interrupted: A closer look at the role of interruptions in organizational life. *Academy of Management Review*, 28 (3), 494–507

- Productivity

- Time for the subconscious to process complex problems that require creativity

In addition, regular breaks seem to be an effective way to control the accumulation of risk during the industrial shift. A 2006 study by Folkard and Lombardi[29] showed the impact of frequent pauses in different shift systems. The results of these studies confirm that breaks, even for a short period of time, are positively reflected from physical and psychic viewpoints on the operator's work. Proper design of a work/rest schedule that involves frequency, duration, and timing of rest breaks may be effective in improving workers' comfort, health, and productivity. Unfortunately, work breaks are often not taken into proper consideration.

5.4 Competence Management and Personnel Development

People are essential to organizations. Organizational performance is dependent upon how people's competences are used at work. Competence management and people development at the organizational, team, group and individual levels are required for organizations to be successful.

Competence management and people development are clearly linked together: people development is part of competence management and competent people will require development. These two constructs are inter-related and, in many ways, inseparable.

The *competence* of personnel is defined as the ability to perform tasks according to expectations. In other words, competence is the ability of an individual to do a job properly, or what people need to be successful in their jobs. Job competencies are not the same as job tasks.

ISO 10015:2019 established the following for *Competence management and people development:*

[29]Folkard, Simon, and David A. Lombardi. 2006. Modelling the impact of the components of long work hours on injuries and "accidents". *American Journal of Industrial Medicine*, 49, 953–963

5.1 General

Organizational competence needs can be met by developing the competence of teams, groups and individuals. Competence needs that have been identified should be related to the development of people. Gaps such as foreseeable future competence requirements should be identified and planned for.

People development should be related to:

a) the competence needs determined in order to achieve competence in the organization at every level

b) the competence needs determined by individuals as part of their personal development goals

Developing activities at the individual level can include:

a) individual learning programs

b) mentoring, coaching and supervision

c) personal development plans

d) formal study for qualifications

e) attending external conferences and seminars

f) training in the role or function, both classroom and online

g) networking events

Determining future competence and people development needs

The organization should determine future competence and people development needs based on:

a) demographic, economic, political or social changes

b) the organizational mission, vision, values and culture

c) the planned introduction of new products or services

d) changes to regulatory and statutory requirements

e) emerging knowledge

f) market research determining or anticipating new or changing requirements, needs and expectations

g) technological advances

h) changes in the needs and expectations of interested parties

Organizations whose people are engaged perform better than organizations whose people are not engaged. When employees are engaged at work, they feel a connection with the organization. They believe that the work they're doing is important and subsequently work more effectively.

Chapter 6 discusses the concept of competence in relation to training and performance.

5.5 Workplace Involvement: Motivation

Attention and *motivation* are often identified as causes for human error. "Inattention to detail" is frequently cited as a root cause or causal factor in human error investigations. The evidence supporting this conclusion is often weak and determining the role of lack of attention or motivation in a human error is very difficult.

Attention and motivation are internal states that cannot be measured directly. During an investigation, real-time, objective measures of attention or motivation cannot be obtained because the investigation necessarily occurs after the fact. As a result, the investigator must rely on self-reports and inference, which are subject to bias and inaccuracies.

Attention, sometimes called conscious workspace, is limited. If attention is strongly drawn to one specific thing, it is necessary to withdraw it from other competing concerns. We can only attend to a very small proportion of available sensory data, and unrelated matters can capture our attention. Also, it is important to notice that the attentional focus of the average human being is hard to sustain for more than a few seconds. Regarding attention and the prevalence of the well-known attention-deficit hyperactivity disorder (ADHD), this is one of the most common childhood disorders and can continue through adolescence and into adulthood. Symptoms include difficulty staying focused and paying attention, difficulty controlling behavior, and hyperactivity (overactivity).

The percentage of children estimated to have ADHD in the United States has changed over time and can vary by how it is measured. The American Psychiatric Association (APA) states in the DSM-5 Diagnostic and Statistical Manual of Mental Disorders that 5% of US children have ADHD.[30] The Anxiety and Depression Association of America (ADAA) estimates that "about 60 percent of children with ADHD in the United States become adults with ADHD; that's about four percent of the adult population, or 8 million adults."[31] Based on those figures, and statistically speaking, every manufacturing site should have its share of employees with ADHD.

A concept that must be considered when planning quality inspections during the manufacturing process is the problem known as vigilance decrement. It was first observed during the Second World War, when it was noticed that after a mere 20 minutes at their posts, radar operators became increasingly more likely to miss obvious targets. And this happened even though radar operators were attentively concentrating on the screen. This problem affects many monitoring tasks where "hits" are relatively few and far between. Quality control inspections in manufacturing are a typical activity where vigilance decrement occurs.

Attributing accidents and quality incidents to workers' lack of attention, attitudes, or motivations is a common practice. In the absence of compelling evidence that some characteristic of the work

---

[30]American Psychiatric Association. 2013. *Diagnostic and Statistical Manual of Mental Disorders*, Fifth edition: DSM-5. Washington: American Psychiatric Association

[31]https://adaa.org/understanding-anxiety/related-illnesses/other-related-conditions/adult-adhd, accessed 2/4/2021

environment affected the workers' actions, investigators may resort to the "default" explanation and conclude that the workers were not paying attention or lacked the motivation to perform their work correctly. We never ask the next question: Why did the operator lack attention?

Many company programs, policies, and practices are intended to reduce errors associated with attention and motivation. Some programs, such as human factors engineering programs, directly focus on these potential causes and contributors to error. Others may indirectly affect attention and motivation during task performance. Company elements or programs that may be implicated in errors caused by attention or motivation problems include:

- Poor or inadequate human factors design

- Lack of accurate and easily accessible procedures

- Performance evaluation process/human resources

- Weakness in supervision

- Weakness in problem identification and resolution programs

- Inattention to employee concerns

In this section we must also discuss the concept of motivational human error, which is a form of organizational error. We will discuss it using the following two examples:

To motivate employees, some organizations embrace incentive programs where excessively large monetary rewards are given with the intention to promote some desired performance results. When the incentive is high, it may serve to motivate unethical and even unlawful behavior. The high reward fosters self-interest over company interest and can promote corner-cutting behaviors that will affect quality and compliance and even the safety of the processes. On the other hand, reasonable incentives motivate reasonable behavior that is competitive and acceptable, while unreasonably low incentives typically fall short of getting any improvement because workers are not motivated.

In the second example, which I call "Leadership" errors arise when enthusiastic managers promote specific goals (most of the time, production quotes) and try to encourage or influence the audience using motivational pep talks, such as the *whatever it takes* speech, and think primarily about end-of-year production goals, which are probably tied to management bonuses. I know several instances in different companies where the message was transmitted so effectively that it was taken literally by some operators and supervisors. They made the product goals, but in January there was a huge spike in manufacturing deviations and failure investigations tied to "procedure not followed" and/or "human error." My only suggestion to those *whatever it takes managers* is to be equally emphatic, intense, and emotional talking about compliance and quality of work, which includes <u>always</u> following CGMP procedures and rules.

As of 2018, Gallup[32] finds that 34% of employees in the U.S. are engaged – meaning they are involved, enthusiastic and committed to their team and organization. Worldwide, just 15% of employees who work for an organization are engaged.

Employee engagement is determined by factors such as role clarity, having the opportunity to do what you do best, opportunity to develop, strong coworker relationships, and a common mission or purpose. And very important, these are all factors that leaders and managers can directly influence.

In the same book, Gallup published combined data from nine meta-analysis of the relationship between team engagement (motivation) and performance over the past two decades. They are combined into the following 12 engagement elements:

1. I know what is expected of me at work

[32]Clifton, Jim and Jim Harter. 2019. *It's the Manager.* New York: Gallup Press

2. I have the materials and equipment I need to do my work right

3. At work, I have the opportunity to do what I do best every day

4. In the last seven days, I have received recognition or praise for doing good work

5. My supervisor, or someone at work, seems to care about me as a person

6. There is someone at work who encourages my development

7. At work, my opinions seem to count

8. The mission or purpose of my company makes me feel my job is important

9. My associates or fellow employees are committed to doing quality work

10. I have a best friend at work

11. In the last six months, someone at work has talked to me about my progress

12. In the last year, I have had opportunities at work to learn and grow

Chapter 6
The Pillars: Training

The quality management principles underlying the ISO 9000 family of standards (of which the ISO 10001 to ISO 10019 family of standards forms a part) emphasize the importance of competent people and a culture that encourages growth and further development.

This document provides guidance to assist organizations and their personnel when addressing issues related to competence management and people development. It may be applied whenever guidance is required to interpret references to competent/developed people within the context of a QMS or any other management systems standard, for example, risk management or environmental management.

6.1 Training, competence, and performance

Competence is about the ability to meet role responsibilities and consistently perform to a specified standard. Meeting the competence standard requires training and development of the required knowledge, skills, and attitudes. The standard should align with the hazards under control and enable a sufficient understanding of them and their associated control measures.

Effective training and competence development are essential to achieving effective performance. Training provides skills and/or knowledge to adequately perform a job. Personnel should be qualified to do the operations that are assigned to them in accordance with the nature of, and potential risk of, their operational activities. On the other hand, managers should define appropriate qualifications for each position to help ensure that individuals are assigned appropriate responsibilities. Personnel should also understand the effect of their activities on the product and the customer. Job descriptions should include requirements such as scientific and technical knowledge, process and product knowledge, and/or risk assessment abilities to appropriately execute certain functions.

Training plays a key role in the reduction of error. Well-trained operators whose skill and knowledge are appropriate to the task will make fewer errors than unskilled operators. There is a difference between skill acquisition and skill maintenance. Operators will be initially trained to the required skill level, after which it is assumed that they will retain their skills. That is probably true for skills that are exercised all the time, but not for those rarely used.

If operators are required to exercise important or critical skills at longer intervals, a major reduction in human error may be expected from the implementation of a skill maintenance program. An example would be the compulsory periodic retraining program of airline pilots in simulators to ensure that they maintain their ability to deal with emergencies.

The _competence_ of personnel is defined as the ability to perform tasks according to expectations. In other words, competence is the ability of an individual to do a job properly, or what people need to be successful in their jobs. The concept of competencies includes all the related knowledge, skills, abilities, and attributes that form a person's job. This set of context-specific qualities is correlated with superior job performance and can be used as a standard against which to measure job performance, as well as to develop, recruit, and hire employees.

Developing competence is part of the organizational design and is critical to performance. Providing the right training and developing the required competencies (technical and nontechnical) has a direct influence on the reliability of human performance.

Competence is much more than training. It implies appropriate education, qualifications, training, skills, technical knowledge, experience, physical and mental capabilities, understanding, behavior, and attitudes.

Continued training is critical to ensure that employees remain proficient in their operational functions. Typical training should cover the policies, processes, procedures, and written instructions related to operational activities, the product or service, the quality system, and the desired work culture. Training should focus on both the employees' specific job functions and the related regulatory requirements. Managers are expected to establish training programs that include the following:

- Evaluation of training needs

- Provision of training to satisfy these needs

- Evaluation of effectiveness of training

- Documentation of training and/or retraining

When operating in a robust quality system environment, it is important that managers verify that skills gained from training are implemented in day-to-day performance.

As an example of the importance of the concept of competence, following are some of the requirements that the new international standard ISO/IEC 17025:2017 *General requirements for the competence of testing and calibration laboratories* contains under clause 6.2, "Personnel":

- 6.2.1 All personnel of the laboratory, either internal or external, that could influence the laboratory activities shall act impartially, be competent and work in accordance with the laboratory's management system.

- 6.2.2 The laboratory shall document the competence requirements for each function influencing the results of laboratory activities, including requirements for education, qualification, training, technical knowledge, skills and experience.

- 6.2.3 The laboratory shall ensure that the personnel have the competence to perform laboratory activities for which they are responsible and to evaluate the significance of deviations.

- 6.2.4 The management of the laboratory shall communicate to personnel their duties, responsibilities and authorities.

- 6.2.5 The laboratory shall have procedure(s) and retain records for:

    a) determining the competence requirements

    b) selection of personnel

    c) training of personnel

    d) supervision of personnel

    e) authorization of personnel

    f) monitoring competence of personnel

The current version of the international standard ISO 13485:2016 *Medical devices — Quality management systems —Requirements for regulatory purposes* also includes under clause 6.2 Human resources:

Personnel performing work affecting product quality shall be competent on the basis of appropriate education, training, skills and experience.

The organization shall document the process(es) for establishing competence, providing needed training, and ensuring awareness of personnel.

The organization shall:

   (a) determine the necessary competence for personnel performing work affecting product quality

   (b) provide training or take other actions to achieve or maintain the necessary competence

   (c) evaluate the effectiveness of the actions taken

(d) ensure that its personnel are aware of the relevance and importance of their activities and how they contribute to the achievement of the quality objectives

(e) maintain appropriate records of education, training, skills and experience

In the case of the international standard ISO 9001:2015 *Quality management systems—Requirements*, there is a clause devoted to this topic. Specifically, clause 7.2, Competence, establishes that:

The organization shall:
a) determine the necessary competence of person(s) doing work under its control that affects the performance and effectiveness of the quality management system

b) ensure that these persons are competent on the basis of appropriate education, training, or experience

c) where applicable, take actions to acquire the necessary competence, and evaluate the effectiveness of the actions taken

d) retain appropriate documented information as evidence of competence

NOTE: Applicable actions can include, for example, the provision of training to, the mentoring of, or the reassignment of currently employed persons; or the hiring or contracting of competent persons.

6.2 Competence Management

Competence is the ability to apply knowledge and skills to achieve intended results (as defined in ISO 9000:2015, clause 3.10.4) The benefit of training and development is the increase in competence, which leads to an increase in a person's ability to create value for the organization and its customers.

Training and development are essential factors in people engagement, including the management of industrial/labor relations, and formal grievances. Successful organizations apply the knowledge and skills of their people in a way that creates value for the organization and its customers.

Learning is the process of acquiring knowledge or skills through experience, from study or from instruction. Formal learning will often result in a person receiving qualifications. Learning processes may apply to a person or collectively to an organization. An organization should recognize that people learn in different ways. Some people are more suited to a classroom environment; while others are inclined to a mentoring environment, while still others learn better in a web-based environment.

A learning organization focuses on increasing and retaining its knowledge to enhance the organization's capacity for performance. The organization needs to have competent staff in order to be competitive. To achieve the necessary flow of information and knowledge and become a learning organization, the organization's processes need to be combined into a management system. An organization's ability to learn enables it to be more competitive.

The benefits of an effective learning process are increased achievement, job satisfaction and job security. These lead to an improvement in attitude and motivation. Improvements in competences such as communication leads to improvements in product quality and better customer service. For the organization, this leads to increased competitiveness and profitability.

Training is the process by which people learn skills and competencies. Development is the process by which people change and become more competent. The intent is to engage people with the journey towards a personal connection with strategic direction and outcomes.

Developing competence is part of organizational design and is critical to performance. Providing the right training and developing the required competencies (technical and nontechnical) have a direct influence on the reliability of human performance. Workers are expected to perform on a wider range of tasks with less supervision, thus increasing the need to manage competence effectively.

Competence is much more than training. It implies appropriate education, qualifications, training, skills, technical knowledge, experience, physical and mental capabilities, understanding, behavior, and attitudes.

Competence management must be an integral part of an organization's overall management system, and it should apply to all personnel (regular employees, contractors, and so on) from the top to the bottom.

Competence management involves:

- Identification of competence requirements

- Selection and recruitment of personnel

- Assessment of competence

- Certification of competence

- Maintaining, reassessing, and monitoring competence

When considering competence needs, organizations should determine the competence required to achieve intended results, at the organizational, team, group and individual level, taking into account:

a) the context of the organization: changes to external/internal issues and the needs and expectations of relevant interested parties significantly affecting competence needs

b) the potential impact of lack of competence on the processes and the effectiveness of the management system

c) recognition of individual levels of competence in relation to ability to perform specific roles

d) opportunities to utilize specific available competence in the design of work-related functions, processes and systems

Competence management should consider all processes, functions and levels of the organization. The determination of what is needed should begin by evaluating the current levels of competence, including any limitations, and maintaining documented information on specified competence needs as appropriate. The organization should determine its competence needs at planned intervals and in response to changes in its context.

Organizations may choose to use external providers to carry out any activities, including an analysis to determine competence needs and assess current competence levels, as covered by this document. If an organization uses an external provider, it should ensure appropriate monitoring and evaluation of the activities.

Determining competence needs and organizational competence

Competence is directly affected by the context of the organization.

When determining the types and level of competence needed, the organization should consider, for example:

a) external issues (for example, statutory and regulatory requirements, technological advances)

b) internal factors (for example, mission, vision, strategic objectives, values and culture of the organization, range of activities or services, resource availability, organizational knowledge)

c) needs and expectations of relevant interested parties (for example, regulators, customers, society)

Documented information should be maintained and/or retained as appropriate to support and demonstrate:

- competence needs

- organizational related to the organization

- team (established team or more informal group training achievements)

- individual (qualifications, performance/appraisal outcomes)

- development programs and other initiatives

- evaluation of the impact of competence development and associated actions

Team or group competence

Within the organization, different teams or groups will need different competences according to the activities they perform and the intended results. When determining differing team or group needs, the organization should consider:

a) leadership

b) team or group objectives and intended results

c) activities, processes and systems

d) structure of the team or group: hierarchy, number of people, and roles and responsibilities

e) team or group culture and the ability to co-operate, collaborate and cultivate respect

Individual competence

Individual competence requirements should be determined at all levels of the organization to ensure each different role or function is effective.

To determine individual competence, the organization should consider:

a) external competence requirements

b) roles and responsibilities

c) activities related to roles or function

d) behaviors (for example, emotional intelligence, ability to remain calm in a crisis, ability to maintain concentration during monotonous work, ability to work co-operatively within a direct team and across the organization or with customers)

6.3 Typical Errors in Training Programs

Human errors are typically associated with lack of training, or more often, poor-quality training. Without a doubt, training can be considered as one of the main root cause categories for human errors and, in a wider sense, for inadequate human performance in the manufacturing industries.

The requirements of an effective training program are:

- Develop the program based on the needs of the participants

- Set clear learning objectives

- Schedule the program at the right time and place

- Select the right people to attend

- Select effective instructors

- Use effective techniques and learning aids

- Evaluate the program, and measure training effectiveness

Causes of training deficiencies are multiple, including:

- Training not required

- Missing training

- Content not adequate

- Training method not adequate

- Language barriers

- Training environment not adequate

- Instructor not adequate

- Insufficient practice or hands-on experience

- Frequency not adequate (insufficient refresher training)

- Not measuring the effectiveness of the training

Training problems are related to two main areas: (1) the content and delivery process of the training and (2) the trainer/instructor's capabilities. Most companies lack a formal and robust process for instructional design, or even an adequate train-the-trainer program. On the other hand, on-the-job training programs in the manufacturing industries are typically run by supervisors, subject matter experts (sometimes), or even experienced operators, normally called instructors or trainers. Those instructors often have extensive expertise in a specific job, but their teaching/training skills are not necessarily developed at the required level.

The lack of measurement of the effectiveness of training is another major deficiency in training programs that is discussed in section 6.6.

6.4 Training Needs Analysis

Training needs analysis (TNA) is the process of identifying the gap between employee training level and the company's training needs. TNA is the first stage in the training process and involves a procedure to determine whether training will indeed address the problem that has been identified. Training needs analysis looks at each aspect of an operational domain so that the initial skills, knowledge, and attitudes of the human elements of a system can be effectively identified and appropriate training can be determined and established.

TNA is a structured approach, initially developed in the military to assess training requirements and assess appropriate training methods to meet them. Typically, it is used to identify, and support training needs created by the introduction of new or modified systems and equipment. TNA is an iterative process and provides an audit trail for training-related decisions. It consists of five stages:

1. Scoping document

2. Operational task analysis

3. Training gap analysis

4. Training option analysis

5. Training plan

Based on the scope of the TNA (for example, a new role or a new equipment item) there may be a need to prepare a scoping document to identify what the TNA aims to achieve.

Operational task analysis evaluates tasks undertaken within a specific role, to identify the tasks associated with the new system or equipment being introduced.

The *training gap analysis* is used as a measure of the gap between existing skills, knowledge, and attitudes and those required. Skills, knowledge, and attitudes required may vary between different roles performing the task.

The *training option analysis* reviews available training methods and media for each task and evaluates the advantages and disadvantages of each delivery method.

The *training plan* presents the detail of the analysis and should include the following:

- Implementation plan

- Delivery schedule

- Explanation of how the training will be evaluated

6.5 Skill Fading

There is also a need to consider that skills fade (the degree to which the learning decays over time). Complex cognitive skills, such as performing a calculation, tend to be more prone to skill fade than psychomotor skills such as riding a bicycle. Tasks performed infrequently are more prone to skill fade, especially if they are difficult or complex. High skill-fade activities should be selected for more intensive training, practice, and refresher training activities.

Looking for the optimal balance, it is important to conduct not more (and not less!) refresher training than is necessary to keep performance at the desired skill level. The military is one of the fields where several studies have been conducted regarding potential models for prediction of skill retention and trying to determine when refresher training should be provided.[33]

Skill retention can be defined as the maintenance or sustainment of skills as learned behaviors and procedures over long periods of time without practice. Degradation in performance can be observed because the perceptual, motor, and cognitive processes that underlie skilled performance decay or break down, or because the individual loses the ability to access or perform those processes.

Eight main factors seem to be related to skill retention:

- Retention interval

- Opportunity to practice

- Degree of learning

- Method of training

- Similarity of training and performance environments

- Type of task

- Method of testing

[33]Bryan, D. J., and H. Angel. 2000. *Retention and Fading of Military Skills: Literature Review*. Ontario: Canada Department of National Defense

- Individual differences

Several types of models for predicting skill retention have been published. Some of them are subjective and qualitative approaches that involve some kind of self-assessment regarding retention and/or the need for refresher training performed by the trained individual. Other qualitative models help to understand how skills fade over time in relation to some key factors. However, they do not allow the prediction of when competence will decline below an established threshold or criterion or when refresher training will be needed.

One the most widely recognized quantitative models of skill retention is the US Army Research Institute's Users' Decision AID (UDA) model. This model was developed to provide quantitative predictions of skill retention for military tasks, and it is based on empirical studies documenting factors that affect skill retention. The model is based on the following specific factors:

- Number of steps

- Whether steps must be performed in a set sequence

- Whether the task contains feedback that indicates the correct performance steps

- Number of facts or information chunks that must be recalled

- Execution demands

- Whether the skill is cognitive or perceptual/motor

- Whether there are job and/or memory aids for the task

- The time limit for the task (if any)

The UDA model was developed through an iterative process of determining the empirical relationship between the set of factors and observed retention of certain military skills, and determining the best fitting function describing that relationship.

The UDA model contains 10 questions that raters answer based on the task summary and their knowledge of the task. Raters select the appropriate answer and note the scale (points) value associated with the selected answer. When all 10 questions have been answered, the raters compute the total of the scale values, which constitutes the task's retention value. Scores are interpreted with performance prediction tables, which are used to convert the total retention score into a prediction of performance for the rated task.

The UDA model is used to determine:

- How quickly task skills will be forgotten

- Which task among several will be forgotten or remembered after a specified interval

- What percentage of soldiers will be able to perform a task after up to one year without practice

- When to conduct refresher training to keep a group at a criterion level

6.6 Measuring Training Effectiveness

Training is a critical component in any organization's strategy, but regulated companies rarely evaluate the impact of their training programs. The management of effective training provides the overall structure needed to ensure that training programs have processes in place to support regulated operations. Organizations that monitor training effectiveness and strive to improve weaknesses are consistently the best performers. It is important to develop methodologies to measure, evaluate, and continuously improve training.

Very often, the training function is seen as an expenditure center rather than as one of the most critical activities in any organization, especially in highly regulated environments such as nuclear, aerospace, medical, and pharmaceutical. In these industries, training results must be measured. Incorporating selected training metrics into a reporting strategy can help demonstrate the real value of training. Measurements that consider performance improvements can provide a benchmark for training effectiveness.

An important consideration is that most corrective or preventive actions include some training efforts, and therefore the effectiveness of these training actions must be evaluated. However, for most companies the only record generated from training activities is the attendance sheet itself. When evaluating the possible impact of training during nonconformance investigations, these sheets merely determine whether the personnel involved in the failure signed the corresponding training roster. If so, they conclude that training can be discarded as a root cause of the situation. Training effectiveness is not an explicit requirement of FDA regulations, but FDA has expectations regarding this topic that are included in several guidance documents.

FDA's expectation is that firms must evaluate the effectiveness of their personnel training because it is a direct indicator of the robustness of the firm's quality system. Quality data (complaints, failure investigations, internal and external audits, record reviews, and so on) must be used to assess both training needs and training effectiveness. Human errors must be detected, trended, investigated, and corrected. Do not overuse retraining as a corrective action.

The 2006 FDA *Guidance for Industry: Quality Systems Approach to Pharmaceutical CGMP Regulations* states that "under a quality system, managers are expected to establish training programs that include the following:

- Evaluation of training needs

- Provision of training to satisfy these needs

- Evaluation of effectiveness of training

- Documentation of training and/or re-training"

And the new version of the standard ISO 9001:2015 *Quality management systems— Requirements* includes under clause 7.2, Competence, that the organization shall:

a) determine the necessary competence of person(s) doing work under its control that affect the performance and effectiveness of the quality management system

b) ensure that these persons are competent on the basis of appropriate education, training, or experience

c) where applicable, take actions to acquire the necessary competence, and evaluate the effectiveness of the actions taken

d) retain appropriate documented information as evidence of competence

Evaluation of effectiveness of training is also a requirement of ISO 13485:2016 *Medical devices—Quality management systems—Requirements for regulatory purposes*, which also includes under clause 6.2, Human resources:

- Personnel performing work affecting product quality shall be competent on the basis of appropriate education, training, skills and experience.

- The organization shall document the process(es) for establishing competence, providing needed training, and ensuring awareness of personnel.

The organization shall:

a) determine the necessary competence for personnel performing work affecting product quality

b) provide training or take other actions to achieve or maintain the necessary competence

c) evaluate the effectiveness of the actions taken

d) ensure that its personnel are aware of the relevance and importance of their activities and how they contribute to the achievement of the quality objectives; maintain appropriate records of education, training, skills and experience

The requirement to measure effectiveness of training is also part of most of the foreign regulations pertaining to the medical product manufacturing industry. As if we need more reasons for the evaluation of training, here are a few others:

- To justify the existence and budget of the training department by showing how it contributes to the organization's goals

- To decide whether to continue or discontinue specific training programs

- To gain information on how to improve future training programs: physical facilities, schedule, materials, food, material contents, instructors, and so on

The Kirkpatrick Model for Training Effectiveness Evaluation

More than half a century ago, Donald L. Kirkpatrick introduced a four-step approach to training evaluation.[34] His four steps have become commonly known in the training field as level one, level two, level three, and level four evaluation. Table 6.1 reflects these levels.

Table 6.1 The four levels of the Kirkpatrick model

Level	What	When
Reaction	Did they like it?	Upon completion of the training
Learning	Did they learn it?	Before and after training
Behavior	Did they use it?	Before and after training
Results	Did they produce measurable positive business results?	Before and after training

[34]Kirkpatrick, Donald L. and James D. Kirkpatrick. (2006). *Evaluating Training Programs.* 3rd ed. San Francisco: Berrett-Koehler Publishers

Level One: Reaction

Kirkpatrick defines this first level of evaluation as determining "how well trainees liked a particular training program," "measuring the feelings of trainees," or "measuring the customer satisfaction." He outlines the following guidelines for evaluating reaction:

1. Determine what you want to learn

2. Use a written comment sheet covering those items determined in step 1

3. Design the form so that reactions can be tabulated and quantified

4. Obtain honest reactions by making the forms anonymous

Encourage the trainees to write additional comments not covered by the questions that were designed to be tabulated and quantified.

Kirkpatrick also suggests measuring the reaction of the training managers and other qualified observers. An analysis of these two groups would give the best indication of the effectiveness of the program at this first level of training evaluation.

Level Two: Learning

Kirkpatrick defines learning as "attitudes that were changed, and knowledge and skills that were learned." He outlines the following guidelines to evaluate learning:

1. The learning of each trainee should be measured so that quantitative results can be determined.

2. A before-and-after approach should be used so that any learning can be related to the program.

3. Where practical, a control group not receiving the training should be compared with the group that received the training.

4. Where practical, the evaluation results should be analyzed statistically so that learning can be proved in terms of correlation or level of confidence.

In addition to using written and oral examinations and performance tests, Kirkpatrick suggests that if a program is carefully designed, learning can be fairly and objectively evaluated while the training session is being conducted. For example, individual performance of a skill being taught and discussions following a role-playing situation can be used as evaluation techniques.

Level Three: Behavior (the Transfer of Training)

Realizing that "there may be a big difference between knowing principles and techniques and using them on the job," Kirkpatrick suggests that the following five requirements must be met for change in behavior to occur:

1. Desire to change

2. Knowledge of what to do and how to do it

3. The right job climate

4. Help in applying what was learned during training

5. Rewards for changing behavior

Kirkpatrick outlines the following guidelines for evaluating training programs in terms of behavioral changes on the job:

- A systematic appraisal should be made of on-the-job performance on a before-and-after basis.

- The appraisal of performance should be made by one or more of the following groups (the more the better):

   o The person receiving the training

   o The person's supervisor

   o The person's subordinates (if any)

o The person's peers or other people thoroughly familiar with his or her performance

- A statistical analysis should be made to compare performance before and after and to relate changes to the training program.

- The post-training appraisal should be made three months or more after the training so that the trainees have an opportunity to put into practice what they have learned. Subsequent appraisals may add to the validity of the study.

- A control group (not receiving the training) should be used.

Kirkpatrick establishes that "measuring changes in behavior resulting from training programs involves a very complicated procedure."

Nevertheless, it is worthwhile if training programs are to increase in effectiveness and their benefits are to be made clear to top management. He also recognizes that few training managers have the background, skill, and time to engage in extensive evaluations, and he suggests they call on specialists, researchers, and consultants for advice and help.

Level Four: Results (The Impact of Training on the Business)

Based on the premise that "the objectives of most training programs can be stated in terms of results such as reduced turnover, reduced costs, improved efficiency, reduction in grievances, increase in quality and quantity of production, or improved morale," Kirkpatrick concludes, "it would be best to evaluate training programs directly in terms of results desired."

He recognizes that there are so many complicating factors that it is extremely difficult, if not impossible, to evaluate certain kinds of programs in terms of results. He recommends that training managers evaluate in terms of reaction, learning, and behavior first, and then consider tangible business results. He also cautions that due to the difficulty in the separation of variables (that is, how much of the improvement is due to training as compared to other factors), it is very difficult to measure results that can be attributed directly to a specific training program.

From Kirkpatrick's experience with level four evaluations, he concludes that it is probably better to use the personal interview rather than a questionnaire to measure results. Also, measures taken on a before and after basis can provide evidence (but not necessarily proof) that the business results are directly attributable to the training even though other factors might have been influential.

6.7 Human errors and retraining

In this section, I will address the use of retraining in the CAPA context. The definition of retrain is *to train again*. Every time I see retraining under the corrective or preventive action sections of CAPA documentation, I ask myself the same questions: "What is the difference between this (re)training and the original training? If a person did not follow a procedure, why is retraining the solution?" Perhaps it would be better to determine why the procedure was not followed.

Moreover, if retraining is the corrective action, the original training must be the root cause of the problem we are trying to fix (remember the definition of root cause). In other words, our original training was not effective. If we retrain with the same content, the same instructor, and the same conditions, why would it be effective this time?

The root cause of lapses and slips is rarely associated with training. A hypothetical example can illustrate this: One operator forgot to perform a step during the manufacture of a batch. The same employee prepared dozens of batches of the same product during the previous months, the last one only three days ago. Due to the "error" he made today, he receives a retraining. Does he really need a retraining? I think not.

Training or retraining is the appropriate corrective action when the human error is a knowledge-based mistake. Sometimes, staff retraining is misused as a preventive action for such incidents. It cannot be a preventive action because, in any case, it will avoid recurrence, which is the definition of corrective action. Discussing the situation with other employees to make them aware of the situation can be considered a preventive action because it tries to prevent the (first-time) occurrence of the situation (for those other employees).

During our training sessions, we use the analogy that the overuse of the human error and retraining combination is killing our training system because we are assigning blame to our training system for all those human failures without objective evidence. The word retraining is often substituted by *refresher, awareness, counseling, orientation,* and so on, but all of them point to the same inefficient and inadequate corrective or preventive actions.

This reliance on the human error and retraining combination is not adequate. Human errors are clear indicators of the presence of underlying problems in the quality system that cannot (and will not) be properly solved by just retraining. Therefore, our recommendation is to think twice the next time you are concluding that a person made an error when he or she did not follow a procedure and retraining him or her will avoid the reoccurrence of the same situation.

Chapter 7
The Pillars: Documentation

Our industry is based on documentation. We all known the expression "If it's not Written Down, it Didn't Happen". Interaction of people with documents involves human factors issues that can have major impact on the quality of the work. From procedures not followed, to diagrams that are misleading, or records that are not completed properly, all of these can increase the likelihood of product failures and process deviations in the manufacturing industry.

Procedures are a core part of every manufacturing operation. They provide rules to follow and approved operational practices. In the field of manufacturing of medical products, there are regulations requiring written procedures for production and process control, quality, and so on.

Following is an example taken from U.S. FDA CGMP for Finished Pharmaceuticals (21 CFR 211). Specifically, subpart F, Production and Process Controls, establishes that:

§211.100 Written procedures; deviations.
There shall be written procedures for production and process control designed to assure that the drug products have the identity, strength, quality, and purity they purport or are represented to possess. Such procedures shall include all requirements in this subpart. These written procedures, including any changes, shall be drafted, reviewed, and

approved by the appropriate organizational units and reviewed and approved by the quality control unit.

Written production and process control procedures shall be followed in the execution of the various production and process control functions and shall be documented at the time of performance. Any deviation from the written procedures shall be recorded and justified.

Some studies of accidents in a major petrochemical company show that 60% of incidents related to human performance were due to ineffective, incorrect, or missing procedures (Center for Chemical Process Safety 2007).

7.1 Procedures and Forms

When developing documentation, it is important to consider how humans' sense and perceive information, and how they access information. Among the key issues for document design are:

- *Medium used in the document* - how users access the information

- *Navigation of the document* - how users move around the documentation: paper, computer screen, and so on

- *Content of information* - what information is available to users

- *Presentation of information* - *h*ow information looks on a page or screen

Documents need to be designed from the perspective of users. Documentation developers must understand document users, their needs, and expectations, and work with them during the process of developing documentation. Documents should be tailored to their user wherever possible. If only one version of a document is generated, it should be tailored to the lowest common denominator users.

Medium

- Consider user needs

- Match the medium to the information

Navigation

- Provide navigation clues that are clear, recognizable, and consistent, such as page numbers, running headers/footers, tables of contents, references, and so on

- Use no more than three layers of information (no, it's not OK to have section number 6.2.1.2.1.4.5.6 or section 8.57.3.1)

- Avoid circular references

Content

- Provide sufficient and accurate information

- Identify clearly what the user must do

- Use the imperative tone when providing instructions

- Provide only information really needed by the user

- Use appendices for supporting information and details

Presentation

- Use the primary language of the users

- Use appropriate terminology, based on the user's level

The Pitfall of Bilingual Documents

In many offshoring countries, manufacturing plants from multinational companies maintain certain documentation in English for regulatory or certification purposes (for example, ISO), in addition to maintain the bulk of the QMS documentation in the local language.

Sometimes, documents are also maintained in bilingual format, and in this situation, there is a good way and a bad way to accomplish this. Having successive paragraphs in each language is a real nightmare. We strongly recommend having the complete document in one language, and after that include the translation of the complete document in the second language if needed.

7.2 How to design and write effective procedures and forms

Many procedures, work instructions, and reference documents do not follow best practices for controlling human error, and so the written process contributes to increasing error rates. Many organizations have lengthy procedures that are poorly written and disorganized. Deficient procedures are one of the most prevalent problems in manufacturing industries since procedures have not traditionally been developed from the perspective of optimizing human factors. Instead, procedures have traditionally been developed to meet a compliance requirement to have written procedures. For procedures to be effective, they must be used. Organizations must also address the reasons that cause workers to not use the written procedure. Examples of problems with procedures that prevent their use include:

- Procedures are difficult to use in the work environment

- Procedures are difficult to understand

- Procedures are incorrect or incomplete (users need more information than the procedures contain)

- Procedures are formatted poorly

Writing Better Procedures

Written procedures play a critical role in maintaining consistency and in ensuring that everyone has the same basic level of information and instructions. They are a key element of the quality management system and an important training tool. However, poor procedures can be a reason for people to not complete required actions. In addition to being technically accurate, procedures need to be well written, usable, and up to date. Ask yourself:

- Are your procedures accessible?

- Are they actually followed by staff?

- Are they written so that they can be understood and followed easily?

- Do they reflect the tasks as they are actually carried out?

- Do they include all required information and/or instructions?

- Are they current and reviewed periodically?

Procedures must:

- Be accurate and complete

- Be clear and concise, with an appropriate level of detail

- Be accessible, current, and up to date

- Be supported by training

- Use adequate and comprehensible language

- Use consistent terminology

- Reflect how tasks are actually carried out

- Promote ownership by users

Start by collecting information about the task and the users. To do this, you could carry out an activity analysis. Here are some issues to think about:

- Consider both the difficulty and importance of the task to be documented

- Find out how often the task is carried out

- Think about who will use the procedure and the level of information they will need

- Establish the skills, experience level, past training, and needs of the users of the procedure

- Look the level of training needed to support the understanding and effective use of the procedure

- Try to involve users in the preparation and maintenance of the procedure

Procedures can appear in different forms, for example, as printed text documents, electronically, or as quick job aids. It is important that users know where the procedures can be found, and that this location is convenient for them. If it takes too long to find a procedure, users will be more reluctant to use it.

Writing style is a very important factor. As a general guideline, keep sentences short and avoid complex sentence structure. This will make the procedure easier to read and understand. Try to write the required actions that users need to do in positive, active sentences. For example, "Add component A and then mix for 10 minutes." This is easier to follow than the more complicated "After adding component A, start to mix" or "Do not mix until component A has been added." Write actions in the order in which they need to be carried out.

Divide longer procedures into shorter pieces. This helps users to go back to a particular step if they are interrupted or if the task takes some time to carry out. AVOID USING ALL CAPITAL LETTERS FOR

THE TEXT. Research shows that this is slower and more difficult to read than lowercase text. Decide how features such as capitals, bold, italics, and underlining will be used. Overuse of these features is very distracting for users.

Avoid using very small fonts (for example, eight points or smaller) as they are very difficult for users to read. Make good use of open space in the printed text. Cluttered pages are more difficult to read. Although the procedure may have more pages, providing spaces between steps on the page will make it more usable. Try to use the same format and structure for all procedures. An inconsistent format could confuse the user.

Why Procedures Fail

Procedures fail when they are not used. They go unused because they are:

- Missing or not accessible

- Inaccurate or incomplete

- Poorly written

- Poorly presented

7.3 Who should write procedures and forms

In most organizations, almost any technical person, administrator, or person with spare time on their hands is given the job of writing or revising procedures. They may not always be the most suitable person for such job.

Procedures are written for those who have to execute the tasks described in the procedure. They normally can detect how good, and especially how bad, the procedure is. So, the question to answer is: Who is the best person to write this procedure? Is it the expert of the process, the person who writes well, a team of people, the engineer, the technician, the supervisor? Who should write it?

It may depend on the situation. Whoever writes a procedure must be a person who asks questions, is logical, likes to write, and writes well. Their preparation, background, and so on, do not define this. It is a combination of factors. Once the writers have been selected, they should be provided with training on the human factor principles.

7.4 Before you start writing

Following are the five basic steps for you to consider before starting to write a procedure or work instruction:

1. **The audience.** This procedure you are about to write is intended for some specific audience. Who will use the procedure? How much do they know about this subject? Will they understand the technical issues? Will you expect them to execute this procedure correctly from the first time? How much training will they need to execute consistently? The questions will guide you on what to do next.

   Remember that the procedure tells you how to do a task. Each step on a procedure can be supplemented by training that helps each audience understand why they are doing each step the way it is defined.

2. **Process map.** Once you know your audience, you need to think about the process you are going to write. If it is something new, you have the option of defining it from zero. If you are rewriting or modifying a procedure, don't even look at the existing procedure before thinking about and writing down the major steps of the process you are about to write.

   A good recommendation is to think about what needs to be done before, during, and after the process. This segregation helps to make sure no loose ends are left in the procedure. In the pharmaceutical industry "before" implies what documents, preparation, materials, verifications, and personnel are needed.

   When you consider the actions required for the "during" phase of the process, just think about what instructions you will provide for executing the task in the procedure. This is the how.

The "after" on a process map considers all actions to be done after you complete the process. This covers documentation, cleaning, and any activities required to leave the area ready for the next activity.

3. **Your documentation system.** Almost all procedures require some sort of documentation, particularly in the regulated industries. What needs to be documented before, during, and after the process? Before starting to write, think about what documentation will be completed at each step of the process.

   Clarify what information is to be collected and in what media. Define it on your map. If you are in a regulated environment, you may need to document equipment use, environmental conditions verification, materials used, names of persons involved in the process, timing of actions, second verifications, and so on.

4. **Why is this procedure needed?** Do not write until you are sure the procedure is needed. Is there a similar procedure? Can we make use of another procedure with minimum modifications?

5. **The outline.** Once the process map is completed, you are ready to prepare your procedure outline or table of contents. This is where you use the suggested format defined by your organization and set up the headings of the sections in your procedure. This involves indicating who will be involved (audience). Normally, several positions (job functions) are involved in the execution of a procedure.

7.5 Procedures and form writing to encourage good documentation practices and to minimize human error

There has been a lot written regarding what to consider when writing a good standard operating procedure. The five principles mentioned below represent our experience in writing and correcting procedures, especially when we focus on human error minimization. If you are writing from scratch, with a blank document, first prepare your format as defined in the process map section. If you are correcting an existing procedure, do the same, but remember that you have something written, and your task in this case is to improve what is already written.

These principles can be applied in any sequence, as you wish; however, they are presented here in the sequence we find easiest to complete. The five principles that we will discuss are:

1. Clarity

2. Readability

3. Coherence

4. Economy

5. Correctness

Clarity

Clarity on a procedure means freedom from ambiguity, a style of writing that is clean and easy to understand. When writing a procedure, nothing is more important than to give clear and precise instruction. This can be accomplished by the "rule of the king." Kings give commands. They are specific in what they want their people to do. Instructions start with a verb, specifically an active verb.

To understand the concept of active verbs, lets discuss and refresh the concept of sentence types:

- *Declarative* sentences make a statement: "The label is green."

- *Imperative* statements give a command: "Place a label."

- *Interrogative* sentences ask a question: "Who will place the label?"

For procedures, we recommend the use of imperative statements. These statements start with a verb, communicate clearly, and are written in active voice. Passive verbs and statements are a weaker method of expressing action and can introduce a great deal of ambiguity into a procedure. Passive verbs are formed with the verb "to be." If you see them in your procedures, consider rewriting them into active, imperative voice.

By starting the action step with a verb, the user immediately recognizes the action to be done, which results in better attention and comprehension of what is expected.

A poor action step for a procedure will read like this:

"This action step requires pieces X and Y and screw Z, immediately after locating piece X and B, insert Y into X while pressing, and turning the tall handle to the left, and tightening the screw."

This is a long sentence with too many verbs. To provide clarity, each action must have one verb only. See the difference in impact with an easier-to- read checklist format:

1. Locate pieces X and Y

2. Locate screw Z

3. Insert Y into X

4. Press Y into X

5. Turn the tall handle to the left

6. Tighten the screw

Clarity also implies freedom from ambiguity. Sometimes, we write a procedure having in mind what we know about the process. However, we need to assume nothing. A statement such as the one following starts with an active verb; it can be segregated in three statements, but the portion related to "make sure . . ." has a high level of ambiguity.

"Inspect the area and equipment and make sure it is in adequate condition for production."

Any "make sure" needs to have a criterion defined. Do we use a checklist? What is the meaning of "adequate condition for production"?

To minimize confusion and human error, we need to be clearer. The instruction above will be converted into three specific commands:

1. Inspect the area

2. Inspect the equipment

3. Evaluate whether both are visibly clean

Readability

This refers to using standard terms in the native language, being positive, emphasizing important information, and properly using quantitative information and conditional statements.

Complex words may look nice for high-level people, but people who normally execute need common words, something easy to understand. Avoid fancy words and you will minimize errors.

Negative sentences are harder to understand, and they are typically wordier. When writing procedures, you must focus on what the reader needs to do instead of what you want them not to do. Readers find it easier to understand positive statements. As an example, note that the following negative statements are easier to read when written positively:

- "Do not press the start button until the door is not open" or "Press the start button when the door is closed."

- "Do not overfill the tank" or "Fill the tank to the mark labeled as maximum."

- "Do not operate the equipment without safety guards" or "Place safety guards before operating the equipment."

Emphasizing Important Information

When writing procedures, there are words or phrases we like to emphasize. For this we can use capitals, bold letters, italics, colors, highlighting, or any other way we are allowed based on the software we use. The important thing to consider is that we cannot abuse of the use of any emphasis because eventually everything may look the same, and the highlight loses its purpose. Also, it is necessary to be consistent throughout the document.

A phrase like "NO smoking allowed" presents several interesting construction clues. It is a negative statement, but on occasion negative statements have a place - particularly when dealing with safety or health issues. The word "NO" is written both in capital letters and bold type. This is a great use of a NO. You want to highlight that it is not allowed, so you use double highlighting.

Quantitative Information

There are many deviations associated with the following kind of instructions:

"Keep the room temperature at $72°F \pm 5°F$"

Consider a change to the following format:

"Keep the room temperature between $67°F$ and $77°F$"

Coherence

This is a property of well-written texts, and in a procedure, coherence means a way by which all steps take the user into the execution of something that not only makes sense, but is consistent, logical, and integrated.

The coherence principle also focuses on anything we incorporate in procedures that may divert our attention from what we are *doing*; this includes "notes," "warnings," "references," and so on.

If notes must be used in procedures, they need to be written immediately where needed. Notes can be used to expand an explanation, present a definition, or present an example. Notes are an excellent way to clarify safety precautions. But do not abuse the use of notes. My recommendation is to use no more than one note per action step.

Referencing and branching are the principal reasons behind human errors in procedures. Let's analyze these two factors that make procedures lose their coherence. These two concepts guide us to move into another place out of the current step in the procedure.

The *reference* guides the reader inside the same procedure or into other procedures or documents but always brings us back to the departure point. One example of a reference might be "Execute the cleaning operation following Procedure 123." Here you are expected to pull out Procedure 123 and execute the operation, then continue with the next step. There are specific words that indicate that you have a reference. These are "following," "in accordance with," and "refer to."

Be very careful with references and the way you write them. The user must not feel that they are constantly going back and forth from the procedure to the reference to get the information they need to execute a task. You write to make the job easier for the user, never to make it easier for you. Thus, a procedure might seem short and easy to write, but the user may find that to execute she needs 10 or 20 additional SOPs or documents outside the procedure. Avoid this!

Branching is an extremely dangerous term when it refers to procedures. This is when you ask the user to jump steps—to go outside to another procedure to execute some steps only—usually when you want to avoid duplicating something from another procedure in your procedure. Once again, consider your SOP user, and make it easy for them, not for you. The branch asks the user to go to another step or document, but the user is not expected to continue the same step.

Example: "If major cleaning applies, go to section 3, step 13."

What you need to be very careful about is that if you add another step, then this branch may become incorrect. Section 3 may later be section 4, or step 13 may become step 15. Imagine your user executing the wrong steps. For this reason, we do not recommend referencing any specific step number.

There are very specific words that indicate a branch: "go to . . ." "proceed to . . ." "return to . . ." "repeat . . ."

Economy

This principle relates to eliminating redundancy, unnecessary prepositions, jargon, and dead construction. Procedures need to be lean; we want them specific, short, and precise. A procedure is not a book. We do not need to write with fancy words or an excess of words. A procedure does not need paragraphs. Sentences need to be written briefly, easy to follow. Long sentences tend to have more than one verb, and they tend to confuse. Here is an example from a procedure:

"Toward the end of the process, add about 10 kg of material."

Imagine that you are an operator, and you see this instruction. Think of a process that takes three hours. What is meant by "*toward the end of the process*"? Is it 15 minutes before, five minutes, one minute? And then what exactly does "*add about 10 kg of material*" mean? Isn't this complex? Is 8 good? Is 12 good? What material are we referring to?

When we use prepositions this way, leaving the options too open, the instruction becomes ambiguous and confusing, and the final result may be a disaster. For this reason, we recommend that a procedure writer must say exactly what she wants as an action—very specific and without any opportunity to assume.

In summary, when we talk about economy, my recommendation is to examine your procedure for any paragraph that can be cut. Rephrase sentences by using only one active verb per command. Separate the sentences to make them easier to read, and say what you want people to do, not what you want them not to do.

Correctness

Now that you have applied all the other principles, it is time to evaluate whether what you have left of your procedure is written properly, with adequate grammar, and so on. As I say in all my seminars, there are many rules for proper grammar, as well as many books on how to use and select the proper words.

The difficulty we discovered when we encountered a grammar error in our procedures is that it stops our brain process. We immediately think about the person who wrote the procedure and those who approved it; we cannot believe they missed the error. The reality is that there are grammar errors that could create a human error at the moment of execution and others that have no consequence on the procedure. In the discussion in the following section, we will emphasize those grammar errors that can affect the actions of the person following the procedure.

In summary, this principle refers to using correct grammar, using simple words and terms, writing in the proper sequence, and supporting the user in their execution. In many situations, the SOP writer makes it easy for himself, but forgets that every time the user uses the procedure it may be a nightmare trying to understand and follow what is written.

When the brain detects an error, it stops. First to try to understand and decode the error, second to assume what is expected, and third to execute what they believe must be done.

Chapter 8
Leadership Development

L
ack of adequate leadership represents the single, most important, and critical root cause for poor and inadequate quality culture. This Chapter focus on five simple, but key questions developed by Peter Drucker[35]. Those questions were developed to help leaders and company executives to perform a self-assessment process regarding what they are doing, why they are doing it, and what they must do to improve their organization's performance.

1. What is our mission?

2. Who is our customer?

3. What does the customer value?

4. What are our results?

5. What is our plan?

These questions are essential and relevant, and they can be applied to organizations from any sector and any size. They can be a foundational tool for new manager and leadership development

[35]Drucker, Peter F., Hesselbein, Frances and Kuhl, Joan S. 2015. *Peter Drucker's Five Most Important Questions*. Hoboken: John Wiley & Sons, Inc.

programs. Taken together, Peter Drucker's five questions are powerful and get right to the heart of what makes a strong leadership and ultimately, a business successful.

We can think about effective leadership as a pre-requisite to establish and sustain a strong, positive quality and compliance culture. Leadership development is a never-ending journey, and we encourage leaders of any sector, but most importantly from the medical product manufacturer sector, to periodically use this self-assessment tool to evaluate their organization and to provide organizational, strategic direction to whole organization.

What is our mission?

Every business needs a reason to be, and this is most often summarized in a concisely-worded mission statement. This should not be an elaborate document that you file away in a drawer somewhere, but one that your organization and your people live every day. Says Drucker, "The effective mission statement is short and sharply focused. It should fit on a T-shirt. The mission says why you do what you do, not the means by which you do it."

Some more specific questions that may help you find the answers you seek:

- What is the current mission?

- What are our challenges?

- What are our opportunities?

- Does the mission need to be revisited?

Who is our customer?

In business, customer is someone you must satisfy. If you do not, you have no results. And soon you may have no business. In many cases, a company's leaders are uncertain about who, exactly, their customers are. And even if they have some idea, these leaders fail to make their customers the primary focus of their attention.

According to Drucker, "Answering the question 'Who is our customer?' provides the basis for determining what customers value, defining your results, and developing the plan." Once you figure out who your customers are, then focus your efforts on satisfying their needs. Drucker recommends seeking into the following questions:

- Who is our primary customer?

- Who are our supporting customers?

- How will our customer change?

In our industry there are different customers including the ultimate one: our patients who should benefit from using our medical products. Our two most important customers are:

- Regulatory authorities

- Patients

The mission of the U.S. FDA is established as follow[36]:

> The Food and Drug Administration is responsible for protecting the public health by ensuring the safety, efficacy, and security of human and veterinary drugs, biological products, and medical devices; and by ensuring the safety of our nation's food supply, cosmetics, and products that emit radiation.

In our industry, all leaders must have a profound knowledge of regulations. Sadly, many leaders and managers think that quality and compliance is the specific responsibility of the quality organization. They are totally wrong because quality and compliance are everyone's responsibility.

What does the customer value?

The natural next step is to figure out what it is that your customer values and what they are willing to pay for. However, this may not be an easy question to answer. Drucker writes, "The question *What do*

---

[36]https://www.fda.gov/about-fda/what-we-do#mission, accessed 2-05-2021

customers value? - what satisfies their needs, wants, and aspiration - is so complicated that it can only be answered by customers themselves." While this may be the most important of the five questions, he says, it's also the one that businesses most often fail to ask themselves. The following questions are related to this item:

- What do we believe our primary and supporting customers value?

- What knowledge do we need to gain from our customers?

- How will I participate in gaining this knowledge?

What are our results?

Every initiative you undertake will have results, which will need to be collected and reviewed. Says Drucker, "Progress and achievement can be appraised in qualitative and quantitative terms. These two types of measures are interwoven -- they shed light on one another -- and both are necessary to illuminate in what ways and to what extent lives are being changed." You should make sure you know not just what your results are, but how you can evaluate them.

- How do we define results for our organization?

- Are we successful?

- How should we define results?

- What must we strengthen or abandon?

What is our plan?

Given how quickly everything changes today, it's more important to have a plan than ever before. For a plan to be effective, it should comprise certain elements. According to Drucker, "A plan ... is a concise summation of the organization's purpose and future direction. The plan encompasses mission, vision, goals, objectives, action steps, a budget, and appraisal." If you can't answer this question, you won't know where you're going or how you're getting there. A few questions may help you find the answer you seek:

- Should the mission be changed?

- What are our goals?

Chapter 9
Epilogue: The Dirty Dozen
of Compliance

Following is a list of twelve areas ("The Dirty Dozen") where an overwhelming majority of pharmaceutical companies need a comprehensive overhaul to reduce their risk of lack of compliance and quality problems.

1. Training and education

- Inadequate and insufficient CGMP trainings (including both new hires and periodic refresher). This is a very neglected area across the pharmaceutical industry.

- Training is more than reading SOPs. Companies need profound knowledge in compliance and technical areas, including a knowledgeable and capable leadership and management.

- No cross-training programs between areas and departments.

- Lack of measurement of training effectiveness.

- Lack of adequate competence management program in place.

- Abuse of retraining. Need to ask: why the original training was not effective?

2. Investigation of deviations, OOS, OOT and complaints

- Lack of investigation plans.

- Timeliness (or lack thereof) for completion of investigations.

- Lack of realistic due dates.

- Everything is an isolated event (lack of adequate trending).

- Root causes are not identified.

- Root causes are identified but not corrected.

- The symptom is corrected instead of the cause.

- Laboratory investigation phase II only includes review of batch record, no evaluation of product history, process capability, and so on.

- Investigation and CAPA program are not risk-based. FDA does expect the manufacturer to develop procedures for assessing the risk associated to each situation, the actions that need to be taken for different levels of risk, and how to correct or prevent the problem from recurring, depending on that risk assessment.

3. Investigation of human errors

- Lack of human factor program.

- Lack of understanding *why human err*.

- Overuse of the human error and retraining combination. Human errors cannot be eliminated nor even significantly reduced by simply telling operators to be more careful. This simplistic approach does not work because you are not addressing any root cause. Human error is more a symptom than a cause. Always ask why the human made the mistake.

4. Invalidation of OOS

- Inadequate invalidation process.

- Testing results including OOS/OOT are invalidated despite inconclusive, not clear root cause/objective evidence of any laboratory error. An example: *"there might be probability that inadvertently analyst might have performed some error which is unidentified"*.

- Invalidation by retest.

5. Corrective and preventive action plans

- Inadequate CAPA plans missing required elements (correction, corrective actions, preventive actions, implementation, and effectiveness verification information).

- Lack of interim actions. The need for interim corrective actions and preventive actions is one of the most unknown and unused concepts in the regulated industry. If a corrective action cannot be implemented immediately, you must establish interim actions to avoid the recurrence of the situation while the permanent corrective action is implemented.

- Lack of true preventive actions. Most companies are in the firefighting (corrective) mode, and they lack the proactive approach that comes from the trending analysis of their in-conformance process results.

- Lack (or inadequate) effectiveness verification of the actions taken.

6. Change management control

- Inadequate description of the change(s) being performed.

- Inadequate explanation of why the change is needed.

- Inadequate justification of why the change is acceptable.

- Inadequate cancelation of change control records when the change control is used as support evidence for implementation of corrective or preventive actions.

7. Good documentation practices and data integrity

- Lack of good documentation practices is also lack of data integrity.

- Data integrity is more than ALCOA or ALCOA+. Companies need to establish a policy on data integrity *governance*.

- Inaccurate reporting of quality data.

- Careless handling of quality data.

8. Risk assessment and risk management processes

- Risk management is more than FMEA.

- Risk management is not intended to justify substandard products; it must be a proactive tool/program to avoid the manufacture of substandard products.

- Critical process steps not considered: for example, sampling and representative samples not considered as potential failure modes.

- Cleaning validation program not risk-based.

- Inadequate process validation program, especially in products manufactured by aseptic processing.

9. Pass/fail culture

- As Deming said: "The supposition that everything is all right inside the specifications and all wrong outside does not correspond to this world." A better description of the world is the Taguchi loss function in which there is minimum loss at the nominal value, and an ever-increasing loss with departure either way from the nominal value.

- Inadequate process monitoring without process capability assessments.

- Lack of adequate and statistically sounded trending program.

- Procedures for handling out of trending (atypical) results not adequate. In many companies only used in connection with the stability program.

10. CGMP documentation: procedures and records, including manufacturing batch records

- CGMP records lack adequate space to document significant/important actions/steps.

- Procedures and records ill-formatted becoming a source of human errors and mistakes.

11. People development and engagement

- Lack of developmental programs for personnel (managerial and non-managerial).

- Lack of cross-training program between areas or departments, for example between manufacturing and quality.

- Culture of fear and retaliation rather than fostering people engagement.

12. Quality and compliance culture – quality oversight

- Lack of leadership: The absolute number one problem to solve.

- Poor quality culture.

- Lack of competent management.

- Micro (or even nano-) management does not translate into adequate quality oversight.

- Leadership/management lacking profound quality and compliance knowledge.

- Narrow focus/scope during remediation activities instead of holistic and comprehensive approach.

- Setting unrealistic due ("target") dates.

- Multisite companies cannot afford to have multiples quality systems.

Appendix A
Characteristics, Behaviors and Leading Indicators Associated to Each Principle

This appendix shows, in a tabular form, the characteristics, desired behaviors, and leading indicators (metrics) that are associated to each of the ten principles of a positive, strong quality and compliance culture.

Principle 1: **Leadership at the top**

Characteristics
• Have top leaders lead quality • Clearly visible, engaged, and unwavering senior management support for quality initiatives • Leadership and vision • Leaders at all level establish unit of purpose and direction and create conditions in which people are engaged in achieving the company's quality objectives
Behaviors
• Establish company values that include quality • Establish a culture of trust and integrity • Encourage a company-wide commitment to quality • Be positive examples of quality mindset to people in the company • Be accountable for actions and decisions, particularly delegated activities • Allocate resources to meet quality and regulatory expectations • Sponsor the establishment of a quality improvement ideas program at every site • Be Company Quality ambassadors, internal and externally
Metrics

1. QA indirect labor rate: FTE QA/total FTE at each site
2. Participation of leadership in external forums/conferences (preferably as speakers)
3. Periodic (monthly or bimonthly) communications to all employee about quality initiatives/quality topics
4. Every site has a quality Improvement Ideas program
    a. Quantity of ideas per 100 employees
    b. Quantity of ideas per employee per department

Principle 2: **Clear management visibility and leadership**

Characteristics
<ul><li>Clearly articulated vision and values</li><li>Clearly visible, engaged, and unwavering management support for quality initiatives, with quality prioritized over production and profits</li><li>Commitment by top management to involve/engage the workforce</li><li>Speak up for quality</li><li>Creating a work environment with low levels of job stress and high levels of job satisfaction (good working conditions)</li><li>Promote teamwork</li><li>Mindset and attitudes</li><li>Cross-functional vision</li><li>Gemba walks</li><li>Oversight and review</li><li>Availability of adequate resources</li><li>Good plant design and proactive maintenance</li><li>Establish both formal and informal processes in place to ensure management regularly visits the shop floor to observe, assess, listen, and coach the employees, such as Gemba walks</li></ul>
Behaviors
<ul><li>Facilitate escalation of issues</li><li>Promote continuous improvement</li><li>Promote collaboration throughout the company</li><li>Be positive examples of quality mindset to people in the company</li><li>Questioning or challenging non-added value activities</li><li>Take personal/individual accountability (own the issue) to solve problems</li><li>Participate in Gemba walks to create visible management commitment and to engage employees at all levels of the company</li><li>Do the right thing when no one is watching</li><li>Tell what the boss needs to know not just what she/he wants to hear</li><li>Display updated quality metrics (right first-time figures, excellence targets on defects, rejects near each production/work area)</li><li>Communicate (broadly) the vision, mission, and strategy of the company</li></ul>

- Communicate regularly on quality topics and the importance of quality
- Consider (always) both, quality and business aspects when have quality issues in conflict with business issues, before deciding
- Provide sufficient and adequate support and coaching to line workers to help them improve quality
- Model (always) the desired behavior of "doing the right thing" on issues of quality
- Practice (routinely) on a day-to-day basis, the desired quality behaviors, for example, through Gemba walks
- Identify (routinely) and implement (as appropriate) opportunities for continuous improvement
- Conduct survey to assess people's satisfaction, communicate the results and take appropriate actions
- Communicate (broadly) the vision, mission and strategy of the company communicated and lived by our employees
- Enable employees at all levels within the company to identify and communicate risks

Metrics
1. Walk the talk: Managers participation in internal audits
2. Walk the talk: Managers participation in supplier audits
3. Walk the talk: Managers participation in improvement projects
4. Managers Gemba walks: quantity of improvement projects generated from those walks
5. Rate of head of departments participation in monthly Gemba walks
6. Quality metrics board updated frequently
7. Rate of head of departments participation in management review meetings
8. Rate of head of departments participation in quality culture management review meetings
9. Always include quality topics as part of monthly department meetings (every department)

Principle 3: **Accountability and engagement to all level: acceptance of personal responsibility for quality**

Characteristics
• Competent, empowered and engaged people at all levels throughout the company to enhance their capabilities to create and deliver value
• Commitment and engagement at all levels
• Acceptance of personal responsibility for quality
• Make quality and compliance a management responsibility and accountability, including front-line managers/supervisors
• Speak up for quality
• High level of workforce participation in quality
• Recognition of the fact that everyone has a role to play in quality and compliance
• Trust in workforce to manage quality
Behaviors
• Put patients ahead of everything else
• See (everyone, consistently) quality as a personal responsibility
• Review quality issues that include executive level and/or CEO level staff
• Provide people with the required resources, training, and authority to act with accountability
• Put "quality is everyone's responsibility" in practice
• Hold people accountable and take personal/individual accountability
• Establish training on proper business conduct including good data management with mechanisms with hotlines and/or emails to promote reporting of issues
• Choose leaders who exemplify quality culture behaviors
• Facilitate the escalation of quality issues
• Promote continuous improvement
• Question or challenging non-added value activities
• Do the right thing when no one is watching
• Tell what the boss needs to know not just what she/he wants to hear
• Encourage staff's understanding of their individual impact on quality
• All employees can routinely explain what quality information is tracked and why and outline their role in the achievement of quality goals
• Involve line workers in problem identification, problem solving, troubleshooting, and investigations throughout cross-functional teams

- Live the vision, mission, and strategies for quality
- Strive continuously to reduce any kind of waste in every process
- Participation of site management in improvement projects
- Employees have sufficient authority to make decisions and feel trusted to do their jobs well
- Employees regularly identify issues and proactively intervene to minimize any potential negative impact on quality and compliance
- Employees are not afraid to speak up and identify quality issues, they believe management will act on their suggestions

Metrics

1. Turnover rate
2. Cross-training plans rate
3. Developmental plans rate
4. Conduct periodic (annual) survey of employee satisfaction and quality culture

Principle 4: **Sharing of knowledge and information: communication**

Characteristics
<ul><li>Communication and transparency</li><li>Open two-ways communication</li><li>Good ways to informing and consulting workforce about quality and compliance</li><li>Frequent formal and informal communication about quality and compliance</li><li>Promote technical excellence</li><li>Active and ongoing engagement with customers to continually identify and address current and evolving needs</li></ul>
Behaviors
<ul><li>Actively listen and engage in two-way communication</li><li>Encourage honest dialog</li><li>Share information on quality performance with employees/partners</li><li>Proactive and transparent behavior with regulators</li><li>Use Gemba walks as an enabler for communication of site priorities/ challenges and how the area's contributes to the success of the site</li><li>Follow through on pending issues</li><li>Communicate on a needed basis</li><li>Manage communication to continuously reinforce quality expectations</li><li>Present quality topic(s) at every monthly department meeting</li><li>Participation of head of departments in management review</li><li>Present quality topic(s) at every all-employees meeting of the site</li><li>Establish formal mechanism to effectively manage the supply chain, including both suppliers and customers</li></ul>
Metrics
1. Quality metric boards updated frequently 2. Rate of head of departments participation in management review 3. Periodic department meetings include discussion of quality topics 4. Periodic all-employees meetings at each site include discussion of quality topics as part of the agenda 5. Establish a risk-based supplier certification program with all suppliers evaluated periodically 6. Conduct periodic (annual) survey of customer satisfaction and quality culture

Principle 5: **Systems-based approach to quality and compliance**

Characteristics
• Solve problem proactively identify true root causes • Responsive deviation/investigation/CAPA system • Standardization of criteria and requirements • Risk-based quality management system • Implement effective CAPA plans • Cross-functional vision • Science and risk-based approach • Sound methods for assessing risks • Well designed and defined processes and products • Decision based on understanding product intended use • System for careful analysis of product quality (CPV, APRs) • Proper identification and control of areas of potential process weakness including supply chain • Incorporate quality into business process as an operational strategy (Op. excellence, Quality Excellence, and so on)
Behaviors
• Establish proper Business Conduct programs with mechanisms to promote reporting of issues • Manage risk that can affect outputs of the process and overall outcomes of the QMS and finally affect the safety and effectiveness of our products. • Implementation of continuous improvement programs that measure progress (Six Sigma, Kaizen, performance Boards, Cost of Quality, and so on) • Establish and maintain a QMS that has clear performance criteria • Follow clear and transparent governance processes • Conduct internal survey on company's quality culture • Establish site specific requirements (when necessary) and not standardized across the entire company • Establish/follow a program of risk management and preventive quality • Ensure that product quality is not compromised during implementation of lean manufacturing or other process improvement efforts • Proactive handling of the supply chain

• Use documented operating procedures to standardize our processes
• Measure continuously the quality of process by using process measures
• Maintenance department focuses on assisting machine operators perforn their own preventive maintenance
• Emphasize good maintenance as a strategy for increasing quality
• Continuously optimize the site maintenance program based on a dedicated failure analysis

Metrics

1. CAPA plan effectiveness measurement
2. Preventive versus corrective actions rate
3. All key processes must have a current risk management plan that must be updated at least annually
4. Process capability of performance index for each critical quality attribute
5. Continued Process verification (CPV) for
   o Finished product CQA
   o Significant incoming and in-process steps
   o API final CQA
6. APR on-time review (per SOP) rate
7. APR review level rate: review by site leader and quality head
8. Conduct periodic (annual) survey of employee satisfaction and quality culture
9. Calibration on time rate
10. Preventive Maintenance on time rate
11. Equipment/area qualification on time rate
12. Validation activities on time rate

Principle 6: **Creating quality and compliance performance expectations**

Characteristics
• Performance expectations for all individuals/positions throughout the company that clearly link to quality and compliance goals • Develop proactive leading quality indicators and triggers • Describe what people are expected to do for quality and compliance • Establish periodic performance reviews with timely feedback for all employees
Behaviors
• Establish cross functional quality and compliance goals • Ensure that quality metrics and goals are consistently designed and selected to promote/motivate desired quality behaviors • Ensure that updated quality metrics (right first-time figures, excellence targets on defects, rejects) are regularly posted and easily visible near each production/work area • Continuously measure the quality of processes by using process measures
Metrics
1. Quality metrics board updated frequently 2. Process capability of performance index for each critical quality attribute 3. Quality and compliance goals established for all employees

Principle 7: **Educating and training to influence behavior; continually developing people's skills and knowledge**

Characteristics
• High quality of training • Develop a learning company • Establish learning teams • Promote technical excellence • Continuous evaluation of competence requirements and developmental plans • Promote participation in external trainings and conferences/seminars • Current job descriptions are available for all positions • Perform regularly training needs assessment • Training needs are aligned to job descriptions • Training function/department has equal consideration than other major department (for example, Quality, Production, and so on)
Behaviors
• Hire individuals with appropriate technical expertise for their role • Be eager to share knowledge and expertise to solve problems • Promote individuals based on performance and technical expertise • Facilitate participation in external technical conferences and workshops • Adopt a Quality by Design (QbD) mindset and approach • Promote the application of new technologies (PAT, continuous manufacturing, and so on) • Ensure that employees regularly receive training that effectively helps them ensure quality in their work fostering a learning company • Educate and train people at all levels • Develop subject matter experts • Ensure people are competent to successfully perform its duties • Promote the establishment of developmental plans for people at all levels of the company • Recognize and acknowledge accomplishments • Promote the measuring of training effectiveness
Metrics
1. Training effectiveness monitoring rate 2. Rate of training completion on time (100% of personnel trained before implementation) 3. Re-training CAPAs rate

4.	Technical training hours per employee: cGMP, quality, compliance, technical topics related
5.	Level of qualifications: academic degrees per 100 employees (PhD, Master, and so on)
6.	Attendance to external courses/conferences (quantity of participants per 100 employees)
7.	External certifications (for example, ASQ certifications for 100 employees, and so on)
8.	Turnover rate
9.	Training needs assessment and job description review are performed, at least, annually
10.	Job description annual periodic review for all employees

Principle 8: **Developing leading quality and compliance goals and metrics**

Characteristics
• Clearly stated quality and compliance goals • Develop proactive, leading quality indicators and triggers • Frequent, periodic oversight and review of quality and compliance metrics by top management (management review) • Establish specific periodic forums for review of important quality metrics and data (deviation / CAPA, supplier chain, internal audit, and so on)
Behaviors
• Establish quality goals and objectives linked and aligned with company strategy and goals • Monitor leading quality and compliance metrics • Act on negative trends • Management is regularly involved in reviewing and assessing product, process, and quality management system performance
Metrics
1. Rate of head of departments participation in management review meetings including the establishment of action plan(s) for any negative trend 2. Rate of head of departments participation in quality culture management review meetings including the establishment of action plan(s) for any negative trend

Principle 9: **Using consequences to increase or decrease behaviors**

Characteristics
<ul><li>Company has a reward and recognition program</li><li>Positive reinforcement</li><li>Appropriate incentives which can include monetary and/or recognition-based award program supports a strong quality culture</li><li>Establish periodic performance reviews with timely feedback for all employees</li></ul>
Behaviors
<ul><li>Encourage and reward "speaking up" regarding quality issues</li><li>Provide timely feedback and coaching of job performance</li><li>Offer non-monetary recognition to individuals who achieve or support quality goals</li><li>Offer financial incentives linked to achieving quality goals</li><li>Routinely recognize and celebrate both individual and group improvement achievements in performance quality</li><li>Recognize and acknowledge people's contributions, learning and improvement</li><li>Inspire, encourage, and recognize people's contribution</li></ul>
Metrics

1. Quality Improvement Ideas program
   a. Quantity of ideas per 100 employees
   b. Quantity of ideas per employee per department
2. Department meeting and all-employee meetings include a recognition section
3. Implementation of reinforcement programs such a coaching, mentorship, and so on

Principle 10: **Commitment to resilience: learn from errors**

Characteristics
<ul><li>Positive, blame-free attitude toward errors and mistakes</li><li>People blame is not part of the daily business and "human errors" are considered as opportunities for continuous improvement</li><li>Empower people to determine constrains to performance and to take initiatives without fear</li></ul>
Behaviors
<ul><li>Ensure there is no tendency to point fingers and to lay blame to others</li><li>Quickly acknowledge improvement opportunities and problems</li><li>Formally review mistakes and errors and look to share and learn from them</li><li>Implement a human factor program aimed to understand and minimize el causes of human errors</li></ul>
Metrics
1. CAPA effectiveness rate 2. Human error investigation rate 3. Retraining CAPAs rate 4. Establish and maintain a Human Factor program at every site

List of Acronyms

API	Active Pharmaceutical Ingredient
ASQ	American Society for Quality
CAPA	Corrective Action and Preventive Action
CDER	U.S. FDA Center for Drug Evaluation and Research
CGMP	Current Good Manufacturing Practices
CFR	U.S. Code of Federal Regulations
FDA	U.S. Food and Drug Administration
FDASIA	U.S. Food and Drug Administration Safety and Innovation Act
ICH	International Council for Harmonization of Technical Requirements for Pharmaceuticals for Human Use
ISO	International Organization on Standardization
ISPE	International Society for Pharmaceutical Engineering
KQPI	Key Quality Performance Indicator
OOS	Out of Specification
OOT	Out of Trend
OTC	Over the Counter
PDA	Parenteral Drug Association
PQS	Pharmaceutical Quality System
QMM	Quality Management Maturity
QMS	Quality Management System
SOP	Standard Operating Procedure
TNA	Training Need Analysis
UDA	U.S. Army Research Institute's Users' Decision AID

Bibliography

American Psychiatric Association. 2013. *Diagnostic and Statistical Manual of Mental Disorders*, Fifth edition: DSM-5. Washington: American Psychiatric Association.

American Society for Quality (ASQ) ASQ/Forbes Insights. 2014. *Culture of Quality – Accelerating growth and performance in the enterprise*. New Work: Forbes Insights.

Bennis, Warren. 1989. *On Becoming a Leader*. New York: Basic Books.

Bryan, D.J., and H. Angel, H. 2000. *Retention and fading of military skills: literature review*. Canada Department of National Defense.

Center for Chemical Process Safety. 2007. *Human Factors Methods for Improving Performance in the Process Industries*. New Jersey: Wiley-Interscience.

Clifton, Jim and Jim Harter. 2019. *It's the Manager*. New York: Gallup Press.

Crosby, Phillip B. 1980. *Quality Is Free*. New York: Penguin Group.

Daniels, Aubrey C. 2016. *Bringing Out the Best in People*. 3rd ed. New York: McGraw Hill.

Deming, William E. 1982. Out of Crisis. Cambridge: MIT.

Drucker, Peter F., Hesselbein, Frances and Kuhl, Joan S. 2015. *Peter Drucker's Five Most Important Questions*. Hoboken: John Wiley & Sons, Inc.

Food and Drug Administration (FDA). 2006. *Quality Systems Approach to Pharmaceutical CGMP*. Guidance for Industry. Washington: FDA.

_____.2015. *Request for Quality Metrics*. Guidance for Industry. Draft Guidance. Washington: FDA.

_____.2016. Submission of Quality Metrics Data. Guidance for Industry. Draft Guidance. Washington: FDA.

Folkard, Simon, and David A. Lombardi. 2006. Modelling the impact of the components of long work hours on injuries and "accidents". *American Journal of Industrial Medicine*, 49, 953–963.

Fournies, Ferdinad F. 1999. *Why employees don't do what they're supposed to do and what to do about it.* New York: McGraw Hill.

International Organization for Standardization (ISO). 2015. ISO 9001:2015 *Quality management systems-Requirements.* Geneva: ISO.

_____. 2016. ISO 13485:2016 *Medical devices — Quality management systems -Requirements for regulatory purposes.* Geneva: ISO.

_____. 2019. ISO 10015:2019 *Quality management – Guidelines for competence management and people development.* Geneva: ISO.

_____. 2020. ISO 10018:2020 *Quality management – Guidance for people engagement.* Geneva: ISO.

ISPE. 2017. *Culture Excellence Report April 2017.* Bethesda: ISPE

Jett, Quintus R., Jennifer M. George. 2003. Work interrupted: A closer look at the role of interruptions in organizational life. *Academy of Management Review*, 28 (3), 494–507.

Juran, Joseph M. 1989. *Juran on Leadership for Quality. An Executive Handbook.* New York: The Free Press.

Kirkpatrick, Donald L. and James D. Kirkpatrick. (2006). *Evaluating Training Programs.* 3rd ed. San Francisco: Berrett-Koehler Publishers.

LeBoeuf, Michael. 1985. *The greatest Management Principle in the World.* New York: Putnam.

Maxwell, John C. 1998. *The 21 irrefutable laws of leadership: Follow them and people will follow you.* Nashville: Thomas Nelson, Inc.

Patel, Pritesh et al. 2015. "Quality Culture Survey Report." *PDA J. Pharm Sci and Tech*, 69: 631-642.

PDA. 2015. *PDA Survey: 2014 Quality Culture Metric.* Bethesda: PDA.

Rodríguez-Pérez, José. 2018. *Human Error Reduction in Manufacturing.* Milwaukee: ASQ Quality Press.

Schein Edgar H. 2009. *The Corporate Culture Survival Guide.* San Francisco: Jossey-Bass.

Schein, Edgar H. 2010. *Organizational Culture and Leadership.* 4th
ed. San Francisco: Jossey-Bass.
Sertkaya, A., Berlind, A, Lange, R. and Zink. D. 2006. Top ten food
safety problems in the United States food processing industry.
Food Protection Trends, 26(5): 310-315.
University of St. Gallen. 2019. *FDA Quality Metrics Research 3rd
Year Report December 2019.* Switzerland.
Weick, Karl E., Sutcliffe, K.M., Obstfeld, D. (1999). Organizing for
high reliability: process of collective mindfulness In: Sutton, R.
Staw, B. (eds.), *Research in Organizational Behavior*, Vol. 21 JAI,
Greenwich, CT: pp, 81-124.
Weick, Karl E. and Kathleen M. Sutcliffe. 2007. *Managing the
Unexpected.* 2nd. ed. San Francisco: Jossey-Bass.
Yiannas, Frank. 2009. *Food Safety Culture.* New York: Springer.

Other books from the Author

Rodríguez-Pérez, José. 2014. *The FDA & Worldwide Current Good
Manufacturing Practices and Quality System requirements –
Guidebook for Finished Pharmaceuticals.* Milwaukee: ASQ
Quality Press.
_____. 2016. *Handbook of Investigation and Effective CAPA Systems.*
2nd Edition. Milwaukee: ASQ Quality Press.
_____. 2017. *Quality Risk Management for the FDA-Regulated
Industry.* 2nd Edition. Milwaukee: ASQ Quality Press.
_____. 2018. *Human Error Reduction in Manufacturing.* Milwaukee:
ASQ Quality Press.
_____. 2019. *Data Integrity and Compliance.* Milwaukee: ASQ
Quality Press.

Web pages

https://adaa.org/understanding-anxiety/related-illnesses/other-related-
conditions/adult-adhd - accessed 2/4/2021.
https://archive.nytimes.com/www.nytimes.com/library/national/scienc
e/032900sci-nasa-mars.html - accessed 2/03/2021.
https://www.bmj.com/content/296/6626/875 - accessed 2/03/2021.

https://ec.europa.eu/health/sites/health/files/files/eudralex/vol-4/2014-03_chapter_2.pdf - accessed 2/04/2021.

https://www.fda.gov/about-fda/what-we-do#mission - accessed 2-05-2021.

https://www.fda.gov/drugs/pharmaceutical-quality-resources/quality-systems-drugs - accessed 2/03/2021.

https://www.fda.gov/ICECI/EnforcementActions/WarningLetters/2016/ucm507554.htm - accessed 2/03/2021.

https://www.fda.gov/media/82570/download - accessed 2/03/2021

https://www.federalregister.gov/documents/2020/10/16/2020-22976/quality-management-maturity-for-finished-dosage-forms-pilot-program-for-domestic-drug-product - accessed 2/03/2021.

https://www.federalregister.gov/documents/2020/10/16/2020-22977/quality-management-maturity-for-active-pharmaceutical-ingredients-pilot-program-for-foreign - accessed 2/03/2021.

https://fortune.com/longform/costco-wholesale-shopping/ - accessed 2/03/2021.

https://hbr.org/2016/04/are-you-too-stressed-to-be-productive-or-not-stressed-enough - accessed 2/04/2021.

https://www.iso.org/files/live/sites/isoorg/files/store/en/PUB100080.pdf - accessed 2/04/2021.

https://www.osha.gov/dcsp/compliance_assistance/conf_board_report_2003.pdf - accessed 2/03/2021.

About the Author

José (Pepe) Rodríguez-Pérez, holds a bachelor's degree in biology and a PhD in immunology, both from the University of Granada, Spain, and post-graduate studies in medical sciences. During his 30 years of career, he spent over 15 years working in a manufacturing plant of medical devices. He also was a Science Advisor for the U.S. FDA from 2009 to 2012.

He founded Business Excellence Consulting, Inc. (BEC Inc.) in May 2005 and since then has been leading its operation and expansion to a global consulting firm. The company has grown to provide a wide array of regulatory remediation and support services, including the placement of highly qualified professionals at client sites. Our people are our most important asset. Their average hands-on experience working in the FDA-regulated environment exceeds 20 years. Currently, we have more than 100 highly skilled and experienced professionals including engineers, chemists, biochemists, and biologists, serving clients worldwide.

Since May 2015, BEC Inc. has been accredited under the ANSI/IACET 2013-1 Standard for Continuing Education and Training which is recognized internationally as a standard of excellence in instructional practices. Since November 2018, BEC Inc. has been accredited by ANAB as an Inspection Body under the international standard ISO/IEC 17020:2012 Conformity assessment -- Requirements for the operation of various types of bodies performing inspection. Our accreditation covers pharmaceutical, medical devices, and food manufacturing regulations and standards.

He served as a senior member of the American Society of Quality and Chair of the Puerto Rico section during the period 2003-05. He was secretary from 2005 to 2012. Pepe holds seven American Society of Quality (ASQ) certifications: Certified Six Sigma Black Belt, Manager of Quality & Organizational Excellence, Quality Engineer, Quality Auditor, HACCP Auditor, Pharmaceutical GMP Professional, and Biomedical Auditor. He is also a member of ISPE, ISPE, AAMI, and PDA.

He is the author of six best-selling books (published by ASQ-Quality Press) covering FDA topics: CAPA for the FDA - Regulated Industry (2010), Quality Risk Management in the FDA-Regulated Industry (2012), The FDA & Worldwide Current Good Manufacturing Practices and Quality System Requirements Guidebook for Finished Pharmaceuticals (2014), the Handbook of Investigation and Effective CAPA Systems (2016), Quality Risk Management in the FDA-Regulated Industry 2nd edition (2017), Human Error Reduction in Manufacturing (2018), and Data Integrity and Compliance (2019). He is also author of peer-review articles covering topics such as risk management, CAPA system, and data integrity.

He can be reached at pepe.rodriguez@bec-global.com.

Index

A

B

C

Made in the USA
Monee, IL
28 October 2021